Campus Crusade for Christ Library

D1592960

More Than You Dare to Ask

More Than You Dare to Ask

The First Year of Living with Cancer

by Mac N. and Anne Shaw Turnage

JOHN KNOX PRESS
ATLANTA

Scripture quotations in this publication followed by the letters KJV are from the King James Version of the Holy Bible.

Scripture quotations followed by the letters N. E. B. are from *The New English Bible*. © The Delegates of the Oxford University Press and The Syndics of the Cambridge University Press, 1961.

Scripture quotations followed by the name J. B. Phillips are from *The New Testament in Modern English* © J. B. Phillips, 1958. Used by permission of The Macmillan Company.

Scripture quotations followed by the letters RSV are from the Revised Standard Version Bible, copyright 1946, 1952 and © 1971 by the Division of Christian Education, National Council of the Churches of Christ in the U. S. A. and are used by permission.

Library of Congress Cataloging in Publication Data

Turnage, Mac N   1927–
    More than you dare to ask.

    1. Cancer—Personal narratives. 2. Turnage, Anne Shaw. I. Turnage, Anne Shaw, 1927– joint author. II. Title. [DNLM: 1. Neoplasms— Personal narratives. QZ201 T942m]
RC263.T87   362.1'9'6994   75–32940
ISBN 0–8042–1129–9

© John Knox Press 1976
Printed in the United States of America

RC
263
T 942

Contents

116 22

Dedicated
to
Lynn, Neil, Shaw

partners in faith, hope, and love.

INTRODUCTION

Who? You?

YOU ARE TRAPPED! Caught by cancer!

Fumbling, stumbling, you are moving through your first year with cancer. You want to keep going, but you wonder how far you will make it—one week, one month, one year, one lifetime?

You want a book that tells the story of a cancer patient who does not die before the book ends.

Besides being one-out-of-four, you want to claim your place as one of the three victims who has a successful battle with the disease.

You hope that others can benefit from your living with cancer.

The "you" includes you, the patient, Anne; it also includes you, husband Mac; and it is meant to include anyone who reads over your shoulder—patients, families, friends, doctors, nurses, interested spectators.

Together and separately you are picking your clumsy way through this first year.

† † †

In the early stages, no one seems to know whether you are winning or losing. People around you are waiting, watching, hoping, working, wondering, suspecting, fearing, helping, praying.

1

While you are ill, you find it difficult to read anything heavy or lengthy. You choose to construct your account in bits and pieces—a collage of incidents, reflections, convictions, prayers, questions, notes. You need to know how other people have coped, to build your own way of coping. You do not expect people to copy your patterns for survival; but a glimpse into your patterns may encourage them to design their own. And you know, in theory, that sharing will do you good.

As you work your way through this book, you retrieve emotions which you left behind. Memories of the events push you back through painful feelings you had escaped:

You hate cancer and what it does to people.

You despise being a statistic.

You dread what may happen to you and your family.

You tense up for each exam.

You want a miracle.

In your first year of living with cancer, these hatreds, dreads, hopes stomp through you.

The book cannot label or diagram all your emotions; it describes events and words that trigger tears and laughter. Your stories are now becoming the stories of others, your experiences their experiences.

This journal becomes more than a mere record of your year; it reports your feelings and experiences. It reviews your past and it teaches you. While it is teaching you, you decide to give it a chance to teach others.

† † †

As you bump along through this first year of living with cancer, you rely on each other, you refresh your spiritual strength, you reel from the blows that strike, you grapple with uncertainties, and you push doggedly ahead. You are stabilized by the expertise and the healing touch of the cancer specialist, by the concern which surrounds you, by the faith which shapes and propels you, and by your children who move ahead—daring you to keep up.

The First Three Weeks

Y OU, ANNE TURNAGE, are being wheeled into surgery. It is January 30, and you are aware that the "possible intestinal obstruction," about which the doctor talked three hours ago, has now become "a growth that has to be removed right away." You are vaguely aware that the tumor may be malignant.

But your concern about cancer is almost counterbalanced by your relief that *finally* something is being done to remove the pain. You were preparing for another operation in mid-February—a hemorrhoidectomy. Now, instead, this. . . . Better or worse, who cares?

Something is being done! Hallelujah!

The anesthetic fog cushions the alarm you expect later. Now, in the quiet of your own thoughts, Dr. H's arrogant comment two weeks ago ("Your intestinal tract is a mirror of your mind") is no longer a burden. There *is* something wrong; but the something is not a malfunction of your psyche. An unknown, medical "they" is going to do something about it. For now, that is enough to know. You can come back later and think it through.

† † †

You, Mac Turnage, are glad you have tasks to do while Anne is in surgery. You watched in misery while her trouble was developing. You know the shattering news—that she may have cancer—has not yet penetrated. You dread the panic that can set in soon; best you take care of chores; preoccupation with details can be your therapy while you wait for reports on the operation.

First, you call to make arrangements about your children. The two teenagers, Lynn and Neil, will be involved in sports at school until suppertime. At this moment your eight-year-old son Shaw is returning from school, with two friends who are to spend the afternoon with him. You call neighbor M and ask her to check on Shaw and his buddies. She quickly offers to take over at home, to see that all three children are looked after—through mealtime or until you can join them. M is aware that Anne has not been well; she is sure the children will be relieved to know that their mother is getting the medical attention she needs. M will not need to go into particulars with them. "You can do that when you know what the results are and when you see them face-to-face," she adds.

Your next call is to L, a close friend of the whole family, to let her know what is going on and to cancel Anne's plans for next week. The conference was to be an opportunity for her to be trained as a consultant in adult education in the church, a training course for work the two of you are to do through the coming year. L may have to get another candidate to fill the reservation, but in any case you want her to know right away because she has been concerned about Anne's health. You know that she wants to know; and you need the conversation with a friend to help fill the heavy time.

L offers to drop what she is doing at the office, to wait with you at the hospital. You respond, "As soon as I finish some telephone calls, I want to be alone. Thanks anyway. We'll tell you about the reports this evening. The surgery may last as long as three hours, so I'll talk with the children after supper."

You call your office to cancel your appointments and let people there know where you are. They assure you that they can handle your work while you are occupied at the hospital.

The time drags, no matter how you try to push the hands of the clock by mental force.

✝ ✝ ✝

Next, you find a quiet corner in a waiting room near the sign marked "Surgery" and settle down.

You quake as you recall the scenes and dialogues of the day, your wife subjected to the indignity of pains and the clinical indifference of "being treated." You were jolted when you realized that "immediately" did not mean "within a day or two"; it meant "as soon as the operating room is available." You resented your inability to help her, though you knew she was in competent, caring hands. You hated the uselessness of waiting in the hall while other people did important things to help her. The fragments of conversation with the doctor, both of you leaning against the wall outside her room, provided slim satisfaction. "Given her history and the location of the growth, it's likely to be malignant. . . . Until we get into the operation, we don't know how extensive it will be or how long it will take. . . . We may have to do at least a temporary colostomy. . . . Her strength and her youth are in her favor." In turn, you told him that you and she promised long ago not to hide medical information from each other, that you expect him to tell you the whole story, no matter how gruesome.

You snatched at moments when the doctor and nurses were not busy behind the curtain so that you two could squeeze some companionship in. But you were in the way of things that had to be done. As she was wheeled out of the room on her way to surgery, you told her that you love her; she smiled her echo to your assurance.

You use the time to measure your anxieties and to go over incidents that led to this day. You recall gratefully that Anne had barium X rays about a year ago, part of a regular checkup. The pictures were requested because of her problem with hemorrhoids, a recurring problem over several years. On earlier occasions, doctors had warned, "Eventually you will probably need to have a hemorrhoidectomy; the problem will recur until then. In the meantime, medication can control your discomfort. We'll know that you have reached the point where surgery is necessary when these incidents become frequent or prolonged." You remember that the "incident," when the X rays were done, was not prolonged; you are glad that the thorough checkup was only a year ago and that the recent troubles have not extended over a long time. To your layman's mind, this means that the growth has not been developing over a lengthy period. Perhaps the surgery is occurring soon enough.

You also review the more recents weeks. Anne was in pain through a good part of your weekend trip to Texas earlier in the month. While she was uncomfortable, you both reminded yourselves that the operation, less than a month away, would bring relief. But, when the pain increased and her system was not functioning normally last week, you made another appointment with Dr. H, the surgeon whose specialty is hemorrhoidectomies. He examined Anne again, prescribed a stronger laxative, encouraged her to exercise, assured you both that the tension preparatory to the operation could account for the failure of her system to act. He also offered to take X rays "if you want them." Now, you are wondering if you should have given Anne more encouragement to . . . . But you trusted the surgeon—his knowledge, his experience, and his judgment.

You go back through the last forty-eight hours. Anne's lower abdomen began to be distended; she could not produce a bowel movement; her pain intensified. Yesterday, when you again checked with the doctor, he indicated that it is not abnormal for a person preparing for this surgery to "go a week or longer without a movement." But this morning, the pain was so intense and the area so swollen that, with neighbor N's encouragement and after a frustrating call to the family doctor, you two stormed the surgeon's office. He was not in, so his partner talked with Anne. On the basis of the conversation and after viewing the swollen abdomen, he sent you directly to the hospital, where the third partner was on duty. "You will be admitted as an emergency patient with a possible intestinal obstruction. If examination reveals that you need surgery, Dr. M, who is waiting at the hospital, is the one in our three-man partnership who specializes in operations of this sort." *En route* to the hospital, the two of you talked about arrangements that would need to be made for the family if surgery was necessary.

Already, even in these moments of prolonged waiting and even while the surgery is going on, you are relieved that some of the mystery is being solved. You may get bad news, but you are confident that the two of you, with the help of God and his people, can take even bad news more easily than you can take the pressure Anne has been enduring.

You squelch your fury at the thought that recent days have been misery for her. Why did the family physician not have sense enough to diagnose the problem? Why did he wait so long before referring her to a specialist? And the specialist could have examined more carefully! Or ordered further tests! Or questioned his own certainty! He was so sure that the problem was either hemorrhoids or mental attitude! Why don't these so-called scientific people use scientific inquiry? Why do we trust their judgment? Why does a patient have to rely so heavily on the physicians—and then take the consequences when they make mistakes?

Unwanted prospects keep popping into your mind. What if you soon become a widower? What if Anne is beginning an extended and miserable illness . . . ? What if the surgery is extremely complicated, or if she does not survive the operation . . . ? What if they come out and tell you that there was no reason to do any repair work, that the growth turned out to be cancerous and surgery cannot help . . . ? You try to control your imagination, reminding yourself that you need not borrow troubles from the future.

You find another project to do. The doctor mentioned that it would be a good idea to engage special nurses for the next couple of days. You fill some of the waiting time with visits to the hospital's nursing office, asking that the staff try to locate nurses for private duty.

You fidget and try to read and try to keep your composure and you try to act casual. By the time you have had all the "aloneness" you can stand, your young friend J appears. He senses that at moments you need diversionary conversation; at moments you need to talk seriously about your worries; at other moments you need companionship in silence. He is a healing force on the scene, and you are thankful for him and for the concerned people whom he represents. But you also appreciate his ability to be a friend and to be a willing, personal presence in your pain. You wish he, or you, or someone could speed up the time of waiting.

You are encouraged too when a friend from work appears, with his wife, for an appropriate, brief visit. You will find out later that Mrs. K, in this visit to the hospital, is returning to the scene where her mother and sister died of cancer. As you talk with them, you report that the surgeon indicated—before the operation began—"Given the location and her history, the tumor is likely to be malignant." K's quiet reply boosts your morale, "I'll not accept that until I have to, until the reports are complete."

† † †

You are able to tell these friends that Anne's strong spirit was in control while she was being examined and prepared for the operation.

It helps you to recall some of the items that she found amusing. Four roommates, quietly recuperating and close to release from the hospital, were obviously intrigued and concerned. The feverish activity around Anne's bed brought excitement to their boring scene. In one of your instant-visits, when the doctor and nurses left the space behind the curtain empty for you, Anne grinned mischievously, "The doctor said that I'm young and strong." No need to put that comment back into its setting. You are sure it was something like this, "The growth will have to be removed as soon as the operating room is available. It's an emergency and the condition is serious. But one thing she has going for her is that she is young and strong."

At another point in one of those conversations, Anne observed, "They've given me shots here and shots there. They've inserted thermometers and tubes and probes wherever they can. Every opening in my body is filled with some kind of apparatus . . . except my ears. Shhhhh! But don't mention that." When you reflect that she was only semiconscious and that she could reasonably be expected to be in distress, you marvel that she was able to make smart remarks, even to find laughable features in an alarming situation.

In collaboration with these friends, you decide to put out the word that Anne needs no visitors.

And the time limps along.

† † †

After the Ks leave, after you and J get word from the nursing office that a "special" will be on hand for the eleven-to-seven shift, after the arrival of L and S, the surgeon appears at the door and signals for you to join him. He leads you, Mac, down the hall to a small room where you can confer privately.

Later, you will be able to recall particles of the conversation when you need them. As you listen and ask and try to retain your composure, the messages bombard you. "We removed the tumor. It was malignant, but we won't have the full analysis of the cancer until we get reports from the labs several days from now. . . . We weren't able to get rid of the whole problem. Unfortunately, there are traces of involvement in the liver. . . . One good thing is that we didn't have to do the colostomy. . . . The incision is about eight inches long, horizontal across her abdomen below the waist. . . . The recovery period is quite crucial. Since the operation was done on an emergency basis, without time to clean out her system, there is grave danger of infection, of peritonitis. We may have to operate again during the recovery period, do a temporary colostomy. . . . You can expect her to be in the hospital for at least ten days. . . . There is no way to predict what will happen. Cancer is mysterious. We'll keep a close watch on her. As for follow-up treatments, we'll watch what happens and decide what's appropriate. . . . Occasionally a surgeon, after a cancer operation, when he knows that there is a residual problem, has to do a routine operation on the cancer patient—like an appendectomy—and at the time of the later incident he finds no sign that cancer had ever been present. . . . Yes, that's where your faith and my work coincide. A miracle is to be prayed for and hoped for but not counted on. . . . Yes, I would suggest that you engage private nurses for at least the first twenty-four hours, if you can find them. . . . She'll be in the recovery room for several hours, so the nurse you have engaged for the night shift will be here at about the right time. She can take over in the room, and you'll have a chance to get some rest tonight. . . . I have given orders that she's to be moved to a semiprivate room as soon as one's available, probably tomorrow morning. I'm sorry she has to be in that room with several other patients tonight. . . . How much family does she have? . . . Well, I would like not to be involved with all of them. I prefer to talk with you and to have one person convey my reports to the rest of the family. . . . I'll see her again before I leave the hospital, and I'll be available through the night if I'm needed, but I don't think that I will be. And I'll check on her again tomorrow morning."

† † †

You report to the friends in the waiting room, keeping to yourself the information about the liver involvement. You wonder when you will have the courage to give Anne those details and when she will be conscious enough to hear anything you want to say to her. You and she will decide how many of the details you will keep secret, to prevent overburdening your family and friends.

Two others arrive as you prepare to leave the hospital. They insist that you eat a bite before seeing your children. You notify M and C that you will be ready to meet them and the children at home; they will walk the block to your house as soon as the Turnage children finish their meal.

† † †

The six of you, Mac, Lynn, Neil, Shaw, M, and C, converge in the front hallway. You stand in a circle, arm in arm, while you report the news. You start with the unnecessary reminder to the children that Anne has been feeling bad and that she was scheduled for surgery within the next two weeks. You explain that the pain became severe this morning and that you and Anne invaded the office of the doctor who was scheduled to do the hemorrhoidectomy. Another physician in the office sent her directly to the hospital where the third surgeon, Dr. M, was waiting. The operation was done as quickly as possible; they removed a malignant tumor, but the operation was not as complicated as he had expected it to be. They did not have to do a colostomy. Of course, you have to explain each term to the children, especially with eight-year-old Shaw's open curiosity about the details. "What's a tumor?" "What's colostopy?" You try to convey the good spirit, even the humor, that Anne used as she was moved through the hospital rituals.

M and C help focus the conversation on the more encouraging features of the situation—after all, the colostomy was not necessary; after all, Anne stood the operation well. You marvel that the five of them sense when you have given the necessary information; apparently they do not feel that further questions are appropriate at this moment. The six of you weep and laugh and hug, standing in a circle at the front door.

As you move to comfortable seats in the living room, M shifts attention to family arrangements for the next few days.

As soon as it registers that their mother will be in the hospital for ten days, the children want to know when they can visit. You hedge, suggesting that both Anne and the kids may prefer to wait until the tubes are disconnected. "Then the visit will be more pleasant for everyone," you add lamely. Lynn responds that she prefers to wait until the tubes are removed. Neil wants to see her as soon as possible, but he says that he will wait for the proper time. Shaw speaks up, "I don't mind seeing those tubes and things; I look at them all the time on television."

M reports that she has received telephone calls from a number of people in the neighborhood, each offering to help. She volunteers to coordinate this help. You suggest that she pass on the word that visiting Anne in the hospital will not help yet. M will look after the children when they return from school each day. "Our home will be headquarters. All four of you will have dinner with us tomorrow evening. Mac, you'll need some breaks from the hospital, so you can plan to have supper with the children each evening. People here in the neighborhood want to help you all, so when they call me I'll give them dates. Anne has done this kind of thing when other people were recovering from illness; now some of us can help you. C, you can drive Mac to the hospital after he has a visit with the children. I'll stay with them while you go back to the hospital."

† † †

As C drives you back to the hospital, you are breathing silent prayer-shouts—"Hallelujah" and "Thanks"—for friendships that glue life together when it falls apart and for the ability of children to cope with unexpected trauma.

† † †

Anne, through this interlude, you are aware chiefly of the foggy ease which anesthetics bring. You realize, as you begin to "come out from under" in the recovery room, that activity is going on around you. The nurses are concerned efficiency; you have the "foggy notion" that they are in control and that you cannot contribute to the process now. In flickers of consciousness, you remind yourself where you are and let it go at that. Other things will wait for later attention. Even your wonderings about Mac and the children—or about yourself—flit by without intruding on your unconsciousness, without even calling for you to focus your attention.

† † †

When you return to the hospital, you are surprised to find that Anne has already been moved from the recovery room to her five-bed ward. Nurses from the recovery room are busy with her, trying to make her comfortable as they locate and adjust all the attachments. Your first visual impression is of paleness, brown eyes and brown hair set against a white-on-white background, white skin on white sheets. The roommates are an attentive audience to all the activities around Anne. The next visual impression is the quantity of medical equipment attached to the patient—drip, catheter, hoses, mysterious machinery, measuring devices that click and sigh.

Anne is drifting in and out of consciousness. Through the lucid moments, you tell her that C is present. She gives him a faint smile and drifts off again. She asks—obviously without caring too much—what time it is, wondering whether a day or two might have passed. She smiles when she hears that the surgery was successful and that the colostomy was not necessary. You tell her that the growth was malignant, then you wonder whether you should have said that so soon. You assure her that the children are okay. Holding on to her hand and sensing that she is receiving signals, you shift to soothing, calming comments. Later, she will tell you that she is unaware of her surroundings but that she is able to hear the things you are saying to her. She gets the message that she will be in the hospital for ten days or so, that M is arranging for the family at home, that a special-duty nurse will be with her through the night, that the recovery process is the place to invest attention and energy for the immediate future.

She thinks, according to reports she will give you later, "I want to get well as soon as possible, and I'm ready to work toward that goal." You wonder if the drugs make her as numb as you feel.

After the activities around the bed quiet down and after the arrival of the private nurse, you head home. As you leave the building, your employer enters. He assures you that the work can move along satisfactorily while you concentrate your attention on Anne and the children. "Other members of the team can handle your responsibilities, especially with your secretary W there to keep the traffic flowing smoothly." He also reports that gatherings through the day and evening afforded opportunities for people to find out about Anne's operation. At evening meetings, he states, there were special prayers for Anne's recovery; and he reminds you that all these people will be returning to their homes and will be reporting your situation to your scattered friends.

At home late in the evening, you begin to call family and close friends. You are almost as moved by the concern they express as you have been by the day's events. Your tears wash away some of the tension. Former associates in your work, B and T, give support by their responses. A nurse, T offers to travel several hundred miles with her one-year-old, so that she can look after Anne in the hospital and through the early days at home.

Feeling that you lack the stamina to talk with all five of Anne's sisters and with her mother, you call Alma and Helen and ask them to relay the message to the others. The most traumatic conversation is the one with your only sister, Maxine. In the talk with her, you lose control of your emotions and cannot give an accurate report because of your sobbing. You label these reactions fatigue; you also suspect that you made a subconscious decision to "practice" on her before making another call. Because of your mother's history as a cancer patient sixteen years earlier, you know that the report will be difficult for Mother Turnage to handle.

Within a few days, you are receiving telephone calls from other places you have lived. H starts his conversation, "I'm calling as the representative of the rope-pullers association here, to let you know that our prayers are for Anne's recovery."

Special-duty nurses continue through the second night. On the first morning after surgery, while Anne is being moved to a semiprivate room, the nurse on duty is a lovely, dainty girl from the Philippines. As she and other nurses shift the patient and all her attachments to the stretcher, Anne is astonished to realize that she is being lifted by the ninety-five pound beauty crawling across the bed toward the stretcher. Mac, you stand helplessly entangled in tubes, providing an essential service; you prevent the stretcher from rolling away from the edge of the bed.

Neither of you is familiar with the "puffing and blowing machine," scheduled by the breathing therapists several times a day. You label it by borrowing an expression from a favorite aunt who often spoke of hard work by saying, "I was puffing and blowing around the farm." Anne understands that the machine and its medication cut down the danger of respiratory complications after anesthesia. You, Mac, watch her work valiantly with the apparatus, straining through the assigned periods of vigorous inhaling and exhaling that leave her exhausted.

The famed third-day-after-surgery turns out to be the time when all the mechanical devices develop heart failures. Tubes break; needles slip out of veins; machines fail to register; the catheter gets clogged. The surgeon states, on his early rounds, that the catheter can be removed tomorrow morning. When it fails, however, the nurses cannot reach him by telephone to ask if he will rush that order; a new instrument has to be installed. When the tube leading from the right nostril fails to drain and therefore does not register on the attached machine, it too is temporarily removed with the prospect of installing a new tube easily and quickly. However, a lineup of five nurses—summoned from all over the building—has to work on the problem before the new tube finally goes into place. You leave the hospital, marveling that Anne has survived the physical exertion and emotional drain of the day.

† † †

Several days later, Anne, your roommate is a woman preparing for hemorrhoid surgery; she was recently referred to Dr. H, the surgeon with whom you were consulting. Following a routine visit by the doctor, the roommate observes, "There has to be something wrong with a man who specializes in this kind of operation."

In each visit, your surgeon Dr. M states, "You are making satisfactory progress." He is on the alert for signs of infection. The two of you choose to take his caution as encouragement; you appreciate his honesty and accuracy, his scientific restraint and careful analysis, his refusal to encourage premature hopes. The same restraint makes him guarded in personal relations, you discover; but you are able to detect deep concern in him. You realize that you grew up with notions of the family doctor who became emotionally a member of the family. You are in the process of getting acquainted with both a specialist and a stranger; Dr. M is working against the disadvantage of not knowing either of you personally.

A week after the operation, when he is making his rounds, you ask him, "How are we going to deal with the cancer?" You realize immediately that he is not prepared for your smiling, direct manner. You guess that when he told Mac that he wanted to talk with one member of the family, he meant to protect himself from even the patient's questions. You also suspect that he has not realized, before this question, that Mac has reported the diagnosis to you. Through his surprise, he answers, "We don't have all the reports back from the laboratories yet. We'll see you often and plan our work on the basis of how you feel."

You are left wondering whether he is hiding information—and whether you want more information than you already have.

You are also glad to be alive, grateful for the gradual return of strength, and eager for more progress.

And you are willing, because of the progress—however limited—to get information later.

Meanwhile, the hospital fills the days and nights with its own nouns and verbs: postsurgery procedures, shots, confusion, nurses, routines, roommates, scheduling, checking, helping, offering, hurting, medicines, equipment, anxieties. Outsiders shower you with their nouns and verbs: cards, caring, notes, flowers, praying, gifts, calls, hoping, laughing, asking, answering.

15

† † †

In delivering flowers to your room, a volunteer identifies herself as a neighbor of your dentist friend. E asked her to contact you; she reports cheerfully that her husband went through similar surgery seven years ago and that he is "well and working hard."

Another stranger comes by, having heard of your illness at a church meeting. She appears at your bedside after the crisis has passed—only a day or so before you are dismissed from the hospital. The visitor states that she came to cheer you, and she identifies herself as a veteran of similar surgery. "And, Honey," she says, "they operated on me three times before they let me out of the hospital."

Ministers from the church are diligent and kind in their attentions.

Cards and notes bring further cheer and encouragement. B sends a basket of separate small gifts, to be opened on a one-a-day schedule. Another ministry of diversion arrives in the form of a book of cartoons, suggesting mischief for patients. Your favorite for countering boredom is the suggestion that the patient cause a scene by wearing her hospital gown backwards and strolling through the lobby.

† † †

As you, Mac, dash from the hospital to work and from home to the hospital, you begin to distrust your coordination and your driving skill. On one occasion, you run through a traffic light. At another time, you fail to notice a pedestrian until you are dangerously close to him.

You were pleased that you were in good control of your faculties; these narrow escapes shatter your confidence. You wonder if you "need a keeper." The stress is getting to you.

After these jolts to your serenity, you begin to admit that you are preoccupied with miserable questions. You confess that you are fretting internally about your whole situation. Why should Anne have to endure this pain? Why does anyone have to put up with cancer? Why should she—a productive, contributing member of society and of the church—be the one stricken? Why do you not exchange places with her?

And, of course, there are the more practical questions. Can you keep the household in order if her illness is prolonged? If she does not survive?

You do not realize it, but these questions will haunt your subconscious for months—possibly years. The questions and their fractional answers become your steady companions, prodding and shaking you.

† † †

Both of you are impressed that even professional people find it difficult to talk about cancer. In light of this difficulty, you are glad that you made the earlier commitment not to hide health problems from each other. "I need to talk with someone," you say, "and if Mac and I were not talking openly, I would have to burden someone else with awkward conversations."

Almost none of the visitors mention the fear-word. When they ask general questions, you try to give specific answers, so that the term cancer can creep into casual conversation. You hope you are liberating them to confront the real situation, without veiling it in pretense or prettied-up phrases. You try to be frank, and you often volunteer, "There's a great deal we don't know about the condition or about prospects for the future. We have a lot more living we want to do together with our family. Of course, we're pulling for a cure, and we're determined to be both optimistic and realistic. We don't want to be foolhardy about our future, but neither do we want to be depressed by our difficulties. We don't want cancer to get the upper hand psychologically."

In a quiet moment after tubes and needles are removed, you, Mac, work up the courage to tell Anne about the liver involvement. You both see the situation as serious, but you recognize that you do not know enough to let it cause panic. You decide to keep this bit of information a secret, in order not to overload other people. "They and we know that we have a dreadful foe to fight. We don't need to know all the particulars in order to carry on." You also decide that you will announce to other people that the operation could not solve the whole "problem." You begin to speak of the "residual problem," or to say, "Surgery couldn't get it all."

17

During this conversation, you, Anne, state that your ordination as a ruling elder in the church, a few weeks earlier, was an especially high moment of confidence and commitment. You say to Mac, "At the service, while you all had your hands on my head during the ordination prayer, I felt that I could probably face death without panic. I didn't understand why that particular conviction came to me so clearly at that moment; now, I'm grateful that it did."

† † †

A day after that conversation, Anne, your physical stamina and cheerful outlook are put to new tests. The first visit of the children raised your morale the afternoon before. You are sitting on the edge of the bed "fixing your face" when Mac arrives for his morning visit. But during the conversation, you lean back to the pillow and ask him to call a nurse; intense intestinal pains have struck you. The doctor is summoned and arrives quickly; you are confronting your first bowel movement since the operation. Ghostly comments about the danger of infection invade your memory and shake your (and Mac's) psychological equilibrium. The doctor prescribes an enema and is obviously bothered. A quiet, humble nurse's aide, unaware that the operation was performed in an emergency situation, is assisting. Through the painful process, she is cooing, "Poor little thing, she hasn't eaten at all since she's been here. Now, she has to go through all this." Your agony is intense, but you have SUCCESS! The nurse's aide becomes a cheerleader, "Wow! Where is it all coming from? She can really produce! Look at her go! She's doing fine!" The ordeal, which keeps Mac waiting in the hall for about an hour, leaves you exhausted. The good news is that the repaired area has functioned properly. The danger of infection is diminishing. You send a message to the Rs, "I had intended to parade in the hall today, wearing the colorful robe you gave me. Instead, today's celebration took the form of a bowel movement!"

A reverent "Thanks" accompanies your strange laughter.

Now, the days can become routine. Healing continues as the hospital personnel and discipline do their work. Your roommate is making suitable but uncomfortable progress following her hemorrhoidectomy.

† † †

At home, the children and Grandmother Shaw, who arrived from California within a week after the surgery, keep the necessary routines going. Phone calls from old friends, near and far, boost your morale and give you greetings to deliver to Anne almost daily. You both speak of the network of prayer and helpfulness that is holding the whole family up and that provides healing strength. Before Grandmother Shaw's arrival, as you return home each evening, you find single friends standing guard with Lynn, Neil, and Shaw. Once, S is reading in the living room; the teenagers are studying upstairs, and Shaw has been tucked into bed. Another time, two of your students are playing cards at the breakfast table with Neil, while Lynn is showering and preparing for bed. Through the nine days at the hospital, as you dart in and out of your office or in and out of class, students carefully ask for news of Anne and assure you of their concern for the whole family. Faculty and other friends in the community are lively and creative in their attentions.

M's coordinating service transforms the neighbors' general offers of help into a series of dinner invitations for you and the family.

† † †

On the evening of the eighth day after the operation, as the surgeon examines you, Anne, he states, "Since you're doing so well, there's no further reason for you to stay in the hospital. I'll come by tomorrow morning and dismiss you if you and the family can manage things at home." Your comments include, "We're hoping for a miracle."

Dr. M replies, "You may have one. Someone Else besides me has been looking after you."

Another reverent, tearful, and jubilant, "Hallelujah!"

Once you get home, you are under no restrictions except those imposed by limited strength. The doctor advises you to eat six meals a day (rather than three full meals), in order to keep the system working steadily. In view of your usual mind-set (disciplined dieting to control your weight), the new prescription is a delight. You are not to eat raw vegetables, seeds, or roughage of any kind. You are to rest daily, but you are free to go up and down stairs when you feel like it. You are to visit Dr. M in his office a week after your dismissal from the hospital.

The community of support, still coordinated by M, brings in a complete meal each evening for two weeks of recuperation. On one occasion, the providers are members of the church youth fellowship to which Lynn and Neil belong.

† † †

Neighbor and colleague D, who is preparing for an overseas tour with a group of physicians from the local medical school, encourages you to contact another neighbor, Dr. R, a specialist in cancer research and treatment. D and Dr. R are both to participate in the trip, where they will study Oriental methods of dealing with death and patterns of care for the dying.

When you call Dr. R, he indicates that he has heard through the neighborhood grapevine about your trouble and that he will be glad to see Anne in the oncology clinic. "From what I've heard, your wife has a serious problem, but there are some exciting things happening in the treatment of bowel cancer." He mentions statistics from several research centers and suggests a date when he can see the two of you. "If she's a 'responder,' we may have some really good prospects for her." In the meantime, until your appointment with Dr. R, you are to ask Dr. M, the surgeon, to send reports to the clinic.

At the time of the examination in Dr. M's office, you ask awkwardly about the medical protocol involved in getting Dr. R's help. The surgeon graciously agrees to contact Dr. R and to furnish him with records. "You're entitled to try whatever help you can find. Their approach is different from ours, but it's another valid approach." Unfamiliar with medical etiquette, you were afraid that your request might be taken as distrust, when you wanted to convey gratitude; but also, you are grateful to get additional medical help.

† † †

Guarding against overly strenuous activity, but celebrating the return to normal life, you ask the surgeon whether you, Anne, can make a trip in early March—to keep a joint engagement that was scheduled months ago. The occasion has important symbolic significance; Mac can handle it alone if necessary; but, if you can pick up that part of your life again, you will feel that "normal" is really returning. The surgeon assures you that early March will not be too soon, "If you don't get too tired, travel should be good for you." You do not mention to him that you are already committed to pick up some local responsibilities within the week, as you move back into your regular routine.

† † †

Three weeks after your operation, you make your first visit to the tumor clinic. Even before he begins your examination, Dr. R greets you, "Our first job is to get you out of the territory of the cancer victim and back into the land of the living. How about it?" Mac notices that the doctor's comments seem to unlock your native optimism. The doctor proceeds to cite statistics about successful treatments of bowel cancer both locally and at other centers. He skillfully weaves another mini-lecture into the conversation: "Many people can live normal lives with cancer, but the quality of life for them went down the drain long ago because of fear. We don't want this to happen to you. We want you to live a normal life, to think of yourself as well, while we work to increase both the length and the richness of your life."

You indicate to Dr. R that you are optimistic, hopeful Christians and that you also intend to be tough-minded. In fact, you state that you *had* to be tough to survive the treatment of some physicians. You expose him to your rage about the arrogance of the specialist who assumed that he knew all about your body and your mind—when he seemed interested only in doing another hemorrhoidectomy. You wonder aloud how much of your narrow escape was caused by his failure to find the blockage. You suspect that his prescription of eating, exercise, laxatives, and enemas could have been fatal. Dr. R quietly absorbs your anger and echoes your alarm.

You tell him about the variety of support you have received from family and friends near and far. His reply is, "I have another kind of support for you. I have a great deal of confidence in the power of the drugs available. Some of them have been around a long time, but we are now learning to use them more effectively. We'll start you with one of

21

these. It's still produced only for injection, but we've found in cases like yours that additional benefits derive from taking it orally. You will buy the medicine in ampules, break an ampule open and pour the contents into your juice at breakfasttime at home. You are to take one dose this week. I don't want you to be alarmed if sometime I tell you to double the amount, or to halve it. We will be checking by blood tests to determine the effect on your system and to find the right amount and the right pacing for you. . . . There'll be times when you're worried or upset. Please don't let anxiety sit with you. Call me whenever you need to talk. It's better for me to have a five-minute interruption of my sleep than for you to spend a sleepless night."

As you continue your visit after Anne's examination, you and Dr. R mention that your children are involved in the same activities in neighborhood programs and at school. During this casual conversation, Dr. R recounts, "A few months ago, I was invited to give a lecture in Paris. I wanted to do the lecture in French but didn't trust my speaking ability, so I called the university here and asked for the help of an advanced student in modern language as a tutor. The young man was a whiz. He did a good job of coaching me; I went to Paris; the lecture was well received, and people were impressed with my French. Soon after I returned, the local newspaper here carried a feature article about my young coach. He had been named to receive a generous fellowship for graduate study. The article went on to say that the young man is the son of a world-renowned faith healer and evangelist. The report said that the boy had parted company with his father on religious matters, but that he respected his dad as an honest man trying to do good. I couldn't resist the urge to write my young friend another note. In it, I thanked him again for his help in coaching me. Then I told him that I'm glad he respects his father's work and that it was a comfort to me, because I figure if his dad can perform miracles, I can too."

After this interview with Dr. R, you write to friends, "In understanding, encouragement, enthusiasm, optimism, and knowledge, he is another gift."

Hallelujah! A new beginning is under way!

1

Personalizing the Process

WHILE YOU ARE RECOVERING from surgery—and on through the year—you measure your future by the past of other patients. An encouraging report tells you about successful surgery twelve years ago. But frightening memories of disastrous struggles with cancer spring from your subconscious. You wonder which pattern you will follow. You begin to see that your pattern can be distinctive.

Y and M-A were your friends in student days. The friendship was renewed when your children were preschoolers. Your family was part of a throng who enjoyed Y's family and got together with them for weekend visits, for picnics, or for work on shared tasks.

A professor who could be a close friend to his students without playing favorites, Y also helped other people to feel significant while encouraging them to be themselves. He could be brutal in his criticism at the same time he was assuring a colleague or a student of his respect. He and M-A practiced the kind of hospitality that extended their family ties to include scores of persons.

His melanoma was diagnosed several months before you moved away, but mutual friends kept you informed about his condition. Over a four-year period, he was in and out of hospitals while completing work for his doctoral degree and while continuing to teach. He, M-A, and their daughters made the adjustment, and continued their way of life while they planned for the future without him and while they made room for his treatments.

During these years, family and friends gave him patient support. In turn, his love enabled them to deal with his problems and with theirs. He was not ashamed to reveal his weakness; and he brought humor into his dismal scene. When there were three persons in his hospital room, he invited them to play a hand of bridge.

His delight with life continued until the end. After his death, a friend remarked, "Y showed us how to love each other. Just as important, he taught me to let you know that I love you."

You wonder if your pattern will take you through the gruesome paths that Y had to walk. And you wonder who really won in his conflict with the disease.

✝ ✝ ✝

How will you deal with the score-keeping mentality?

Before Anne is dismissed from the hospital, you are consciously tabulating reports on other people's history with cancer. A neighbor reports that her husband survived similar surgery and is still functioning nine years later.

Your brother-in-law B had a malignant growth removed six years ago.

Grandmother Turnage had breast surgery immediately before Lynn was born, seventeen years ago. She had no recurrence until a few months before Anne's surgery.

L reports on a neighbor who had a malignant growth twenty years ago, and had no further problems with her health since then.

Can you predict—from other people's experiences—what you can expect? Do you want to know what's ahead?

† † †

How will you interpret a minister's report that one of his parishioners was killed in an automobile accident six weeks after cancer surgery? The doctors had told the patient that they were not able to remove all the cancerous tissue. When an autopsy was performed after the accident, there was no sign of cancer in his body. (When Dr. R hears this story, his angry retort is, "Hell! You don't have to die to convince me that cancer can be cured. One day we will have statistics to prove what we know now—that cancer can be defeated.")

What are the possibilities for a complete cure, or remission, or whatever you call it?

> I had a memory of my father whose bout with cancer in 1925 seemed a death sentence. Only my mother knew he had only six months to live, but he outlived his doctor and nurse and died of a heart attack in 1954, after a rich, full life.
> —B.H.

† † †

How do you handle people's pessimistic mind-set about cancer? How can your optimistic attitude compete with public pressure which says that cancer is always fatal? Will you be able to maintain both caution and confidence, both realism and hope?

Because of society's alarm, many people cannot use the word *cancer* in their conversations with you. You have been jolted by the thud that hits a family when cancer is discovered. Now you find out that the same thud has struck the public mind.

25

GOD,
we hesitate
to keep begging,
when You know
that we want
healing.

But that's where we are now.

By Your grace,
we can cope
with limitations,
with treatments,
with pain,
with distress.

But we want
to be healthy,
PLEASE.

Your image is disfigured by fear of the disease you now represent. You are the reminder that everyone is mortal. They see in you their own fear of death. "Will she be here tomorrow?" "What about next spring?"

How can you keep your equilibrium when "they" are thinking, "That poor dear"? "She has cancer. Too bad." "She looks well, but. . . ." "I can see it in her face—that sad smile." How can you confront the silent recognition of the averted gaze or the covert stare? You feel this pressure so sharply that it almost knocks you off balance.

† † †

How can you control your own alarm? Can you admit that you are alarmed? Can you cope with memories of other people who have been struck down and who have been dragged through miserable final months of life? Can you accept your own emotional ups and downs as you battle with this foe? Can you live in center-stage as objects of concern—and sometimes pity? In other words, can you live with the tables turned—being helped instead of helping? Can you confront uncertainty? At the same time, are you able to take initiatives? Can you tolerate being put on the shelf as "sick"? Can you live victoriously when you feel that life is being shattered? Can you confront death with joy? Can you *live* with a threat hanging over you? Can you rebuild after death, with sanity?

† † †

While you are being shaken by these memories, distractions, questions, and pains, you also make some important discoveries. The first year with cancer is bringing the conviction—often reinforced and expanded, sometimes questioned and battered—that each person's experience is dramatically different. You find that you do not have to reproduce anyone else's history with cancer.

Experts agree that cancer is mysterious. The reactions of patients vary. There are many types of cancer and the different types affect their victims in different ways. There are varieties of treatments; and treatments produce different effects in different people. Your bout with the disease does not need to follow any particular pattern. You are free from what you hear!

As you start taking the prescribed medicine, you are interested in the printed folder enclosed with each container of florouracil. However, when you see the warnings about possible side effects, you decide not to read further. It will not help for you to know that your hair may fall out, your nails may drop off, sores may develop in your mouth. You establish the habit of throwing away the printed folder as soon as you open the container. At least, you can be free from the power of those suggestions!

When you take your first dose of the medicine, Anne, you see the family staring at you as though they all expect you to turn a vivid green or to blow up like a balloon. You are glad to disappoint their expectations.

Discarding the containers and calmly taking the medicine become symbolic acts by which you confirm your hope that healing does take place.

You are discovering that each person's experience with cancer is highly personalized. In turn, this discovery leads you to another, more basic conviction, that life itself is mysterious, highly indi-

are not sparrows two a penny?

Yet without your Father's leave
not one of them can fall
to the ground.

As for you,
even the hairs of your head
have all been counted.

So have no fear;
you are worth more than
any number of sparrows.

Matthew 10:29–31 (N.E.B.)

God treats His Creation
with respect
and careful attention

as a part of His creation
as objects of His love,
we can expect His tender care

NOW and ALWAYS!

vidualized. You knew it all along, but the year is reinforcing your certainty that each person is a special creation, an exotic mix of problems and solutions, hopes and frustrations, pains and delights. Each of us has distinctive traits, strengths, and weaknesses; each person builds a distinctive style of coping with life. Human beings are by nature originals, and they have the privilege of developing their own original patterns. Each of us deals with a distinctive set of problems.

The New Testament story of the lost sheep conveys this truth. According to this parable, God cares intensely for each of his creatures. Not one escapes his personal notice—not even a lamb or a sparrow. He reaches out to each of us with highly personalized care and love; he acts to protect and reclaim all his creatures.

You respond to the conviction and to the Biblical teaching by trying to fashion your lives with respect for your own distinctive abilities and problems. You see yourselves as objects of God's personal attention.

† † †

You also discover that cancer—or any other trauma—blinds people to ordinary problems and situations. Not all your headaches or sniffles or pains are related to the cancer. After fretting over a pain in your shoulder, you ask Dr. R to check it out. After a careful examination, he replies calmly, "Why don't you take some aspirin."

In other words, you are discovering that many problems are problems of perspective. When someone asks you how you are feeling, you assume now that the questioner knows about your cancer, and you give appropriate information. For instance, you are likely to report that you had a checkup last month and that you are grateful to be able to report that all is going well. "My system is responding well to the chemotherapy, and I've had no bad side effects. In fact, I'm functioning normally, carrying a full load of responsibilities." You may give weighty answers to casual questions; but your situation and your perspective color the way you hear and answer.

† † †

Through this year, you are also finding that other people do not handle life the same way you do. You do not expect anyone to copy your patterns, you say. But you are taken aback when Grandmother Turnage reports on a comment she overheard in her doctor's reception room: "Well, I'd rather have cancer than be a blooming idiot."

In a more sober vein, you realize that other people choose to handle problems by retreating into greater secrecy. You realize, for instance, that you have exercised your own right to privacy by not telling, until you started composing this journal, that your liver is involved. Other people choose to make public announcements about all the details—or about none of them.

In fresh ways, you are realizing during this year that all people are in the same boat. With all people you face uncertainty; you are mortal; you are limited; you are frustrated; you do fear; you are victims of forces which you cannot control. As Grandmother Shaw says, "None of us has the promise of tomorrow." But each has freedom and responsibility to help shape today.

Without a conscious decision, you find yourselves moving ahead to see what each new day offers. There is no way for you to predict tomorrow, to diagram the future, even to anticipate part of today. But,

> The thing that makes your letter so fantastic to me is the joy and celebration which has been so much a part of all this —even in the midst of concern, fear, the knowledge of pain and suffering, all the hovering "unknowns." When you could say, "we are one body, one mind, one spirit," the rest of us could only feel that it is so, and rejoice!
>
> E.S.

NOW, GOD,
while we
cannot know
what's ahead,
we can see that
we need Your help
to strike a proper balance—
a willingness not to know,
alongside
a determination
to keep going.

Help us
keep our balance.

AMEN.

without accurate blueprints to follow, you are finding your own personal combination of dare and dread.

You recall a story that Dr. R told about the young woman who was engaged to be married when she was informed that she had cancer and that the disease was in advanced stages. When relatives objected to the marriage, the couple insisted that they loved each other and would be married even if they knew that the bride would be killed in an accident the day after the wedding. Dr. R beams when he reports that despite the odds, they have had several years of rich life together. The mixture of dare and dread has obviously been part of their pattern.

Each person has a story to tell, a battle to fight, a victory to claim. "Old time religion" thrived on testimonies, stories that had to be shared, highly personalized versions of life. You make a conscientious decision that this journal will become your testimony, your story of trauma and faith, of fear and celebration, of dare and dread.

† † †

You are discovering and you hope other people can discover fresh richness in God's personalized love for each of his children. You are grateful for the forms in which this love comes to you. You experience it in the knowledge, skills, care, and even the machinery of the medical profession. You know it clearly in the support of your families, friends, the church, and countless people whose direct connection with you is flimsy. You find it confirmed in the gratitude and hope that enrich each day for you. You know it in the quiet confidence that you will be able to take whatever comes, in the process of hurting and healing that is still going on, in the equilibrium of your children when they are mystified, in your companionship with each other, and in the Biblical witness to God's love in Jesus Christ.

2

Confronting
Death

WHILE YOU ARE still in the hospital, Lynn's high school history class is studying traditional American ways of dealing with death. Her project-assignment calls for her and other students to visit the morgue, to attend a funeral, to tour a mortuary, or to write a statement of their understanding of death. (You know that the course has already studied American ways of dealing with race relations, with war, and with depressions.) Lynn handles this assignment without telling either of you what is going on. Later in the course, she confides in S, an adult friend, that the burden has been heavy. S eases her burden by helping Lynn to talk with the teacher about the pain involved in doing the assignment.

† † †

You wonder how much warning you need to give your children about the danger of death. Throughout the process, you speak frankly with them, using the words *cancer* and *malignancy*. They sense, while she is in the hospital, that their mother is in a dangerous condition, that the situation is serious. They also sense that recovery is beginning. You talk with them about the medicine and about the reports from checkups.

LORD,
through Your life
among people,
by the pain
You endured firsthand,
we are healed.

Help us to see
our own pain
in this larger perspective,
knowing that
You live through it again,
afresh with us.

Thanks
for not backing away
from this part
of human life.

Thanks
for continuing to
share with us
the ability to take it.

AMEN.

Now you wonder whether they need to be alerted about the threat of death. You work up your courage to initiate a conversation on this topic with the doctor. He remarks, "If you had tried to keep your condition a secret, you would've failed. The neighborhood grapevine would've reported to them. They know that the disease is bad news. They don't need any further warnings. If they need the warnings later, you'll have ample time to interpret the picture to them. They don't need to carry the load of fear any more than they already have."

In the spring, immediately after Easter holidays, a fifteen-year-old neighbor, who befriended Neil during the Turnage crisis, dies. The entire neighborhood is shocked; but the community rallies to support the family and other teenagers who feel the jolt so keenly. Your sympathy is intensified by your recent brush with the danger of death. The memorial service is designed as a celebration and includes a choir of about fifty young people. The informality allows people to express their grief while affirming the value of life.

The day after memorial services for the teenager, your family attends the funeral for a friend in the church. She had been a soloist in the choir and a music teacher; and her teenage daughter and son are members of the church youth group with Lynn and Neil Turnage. The two families became friends initially through the church's annual family camp.

The mother entered the hospital about six weeks after Anne's operation. She underwent exploratory surgery; cancer was discovered; two weeks later, she died.

You are grateful that you have worked through some of the questions about why one person dies and another lives. You do not feel that you have complete answers to these questions, but you have worked on them. Therefore, you do not have to fret over whether that family will resent your good fortune or whether you can manage to keep your composure in their presence. You can affirm your friendship with them and your concern for them; you can even understand part of the pain they are going through. Recognizing that you could easily have been in their position, you empathize with them more deeply than they can realize. You hope that your love, in responding to their pain, will release strength for them; you also hope that you can manage to sympathize without succumbing to the paralysis of misery and depression.

Again, her funeral includes chances for the grieving family to affirm faith. As part of the congregation you sing the Nicene Creed in the arrangement from *Rejoice*, a contemporary mass. You gladly, tearfully sing the hymn, "For All the Saints Who from Their Labors Rest. . . . "

† † †

So, within three months after your surgery, you are involved with two other families as they move through grief. Each incident pushes you back into some of your own earlier thinking about death.

Your starting point is the traditional set of Christian beliefs. Life with God, which begins here and now, is life that extends beyond human death. We are mortal; that is, sooner or later, we die. By the grace of God, the life beyond is free from the restrictions and contaminations of this one. Life is accurately measured in richness rather than length.

O GOD,
When we get this close to
the edge of life, we need
more than
cheerfulness,
more than
confidence,
more than
wishful thinking.

By the victory of Jesus
over death,
You provide that
"more than"
for us.

Help us
walk regularly
in this kind of hope—
not only when
our own resources
wear thin.

OKAY?

GOD is our shelter
and our refuge,
a timely help in trouble;

so we are not afraid
when the earth heaves
and the mountains
are hurled into the sea,
when its waters
seethe in tumult
and the mountains quake
before his majesty.

PSALM 46:1–3 (N.E.B.)

EARTHQUAKES

PHYSICAL OR EMOTIONAL
shake us up

GOD'S POWER AND CONTROL
stabilize
us

In contrast with these clear convictions, you are miserable in confronting the danger of death. You do not welcome the possibility of your life's end. You do not want to miss the delightful maturing of your children. You do not want your companionship with each other to be shattered; you do not want your family unit to be disrupted. You, Mac, are terrified at the prospect of being a widower, of maintaining a one-parent household. While you develop some skills at controlling your imagination, both of you worry through funeral plans, a variety of options for the family's future. You spend time and emotional energy anticipating an array of emergencies. You get caught in the discomfort of alarm.

As soon as you can articulate these bothers and discuss the alarm, you can move to a more constructive plan of attack on the problem.

You review your convictions and talk out your bothers. Anne, you recall that your ordination as a ruling elder in the church re-invigorated your confidence, two weeks before the surgery. As you knelt before the congregation, you were keenly aware of your unity with leaders of the church through the centuries. As leaders in your church placed their hands on your head for the ordination prayer, you sensed that the power available to you is the same power that enabled the martyrs and heroes of the faith to persevere in the face of difficulties and disasters. When you talk about this moment of high inspiration, you confess that you felt more secure than ever before—secure to undertake the task to which you were elected and secure to face even the final enemy, death.

You also review earlier plans about how your family will handle arrangements at the time of death. You promise each other that funeral or memorial services will praise God as the creator and redeemer of life, will affirm the victory of Jesus Christ over life and death, will allow for open expressions of grief and need, will call for God's help to rebuild, and will commission the worshiping community to join in triumphant service of God and his world. You hope that a Turnage funeral will call attention to the union of the church militant with the church triumphant, to the continuing mission of people who know His mysterious victory over pain and death.

In the services you expect to include ample opportunity for the congregation to express its gratitude and its confidence, as well as its sorrow. You hope to use one of the classic creeds of the church, to have the congregation sing songs of triumph, to have the community strengthened by worshiping God. You prefer for the burial or cremation to take place in advance of the public worship service. You have agreed not to have the body on display. (You want the family and the congregation to be released from fretting over how and when and where to place the casket.) You will need—and other people will need—to focus on opportunities in the future rather than regrets about the loss.

In the past, you have encouraged other people to plan for confronting death, to think through their convictions and preferences before the pressures become intense. You have participated in study groups for thinking through these issues, suggesting that both wills and plans for funerals be written out in detail and placed in convenient

You must have felt the flood of prayers that were said for your complete recovery from your operation and its discovery. This morning after we had gone to our knees Bob's call to Mac was relayed via telephone with its hopeful message.

Strange, but I had already received hope from prayer—so the second message was a reiteration of that hope. Each of us has benefited by our immediate and deeply felt concern for all of you, so you have certainly been a channel for God's love.

C.H.

PLEASE, GOD
keep us from alarm;
it damages people.

We know that we need to be
alert
cautious
disciplined.

We need
a new brand of trust,
so that
while we watch for dangers,
we can also find
signals for encouragement.

safekeeping. In your own experience this year, you are re-endorsing these procedures as sound. You hope that you will be given the resources to face death with a minimum of panic.

You do not view death as a normal part of life, because normal parts of life are repeatable. Death is experienced only once.

You cannot manage the prospect yet, but you want to meet death with some of the same excitement and anticipation that has marked your approach to new adventures. You are not eager for death in the way you were eager for earlier exciting experiences, but you would like to have confidence about meeting the unknown.

You see that you really cannot anticipate all the elements of your future. Although you can figure out some basic approaches, you still have to meet external uncertainties with internal uncertainty. However, you know that one sensible step in preparation is to anticipate as accurately as you can.

You know too that ultimate realities are mysterious. You do not understand why you are given the gift of life (while others are losing it) but you want to use the gifts that come your way. Life as well as death is mysterious.

You need to have these preparations tidied up, but you do not want to be preoccupied with them. Now the thing for you to do is to grasp and use whatever amount of life is given to you. One of the reasons you want life to continue is that you are enjoying it and you see things that need to be done. You want to continue your companionship and your mission.

God knows this, and so do you.

3

Muddling Through the Medical Mystique

"**D**IDN'T YOU TELL me that they took a six-foot length out of Anne's intestine?" F asks.

"No," you reply, "you told me that several years ago the surgeon took a six-foot length out of your father's intestine."

"Do you mean to tell me that you don't know the type or the dimensions of the tumor they removed?"

"No, we don't. We've decided that those facts wouldn't help us."

† † †

You both are surprised that you do not need all the details about the disease. You are content for the medical people to have and use these facts; you are alert to the facts only in general terms. The danger of infection or of complications during the recovery occupies your mind while you are under the initial pressures. You have enough information to set up a plan of action. You will concentrate on regaining your strength, cooperating with the hospital routine, and getting back to normal.

41

*F*or I reckon that
the sufferings
we now endure
bear no comparison
with the splendour,
as yet unrevealed,
which is in store for us.

Romans 8:18 (N.E.B.)

Finally everything will be glorious

fresh, new,

For now we can put up with a mess

You write home:

Dear Mother:

You wanted to know more about Dr. R than we could tell you in our telephone conversation. We were referred to him as a specialist in chemotherapy and cancer research. He turned out to be a specialist in the human spirit.

What we heard about him did not prepare us for his appearance. His full, black beard is shaggy; he is a high-powered personality with a calming influence; his bearing is dignified informality. In this youngish version of a Jewish Santa, eyes sparkle through glasses that insist on sliding down his nose.

We have already told you about his initial conversation, about his call "out of the territory of the cancer victim and into the land of the living." He also quoted encouraging statistics about recent experiments, and he casually mentioned "your serious problem." While we talked, he listened closely, but—at the same time—he seemed preoccupied with a larger reality. Maybe he is steadily fighting a larger foe than our individual problem.

Often, he punctuates his conversation with a "hell" or a "damn." But you get the idea that the man is engaged in work which he regards as holy. He feels that scientific inquiry is a dialogue with God and that creative scientists are the prophets of our time; at fortunate moments, they get insights and visions as to the way things are or can be. A devout Jew, he is concerned about the whole person; his optimism is contagious. He believes in the drugs he administers, in the process he works with, and in the strength of the human spirit. He knows that we need to trust him. In his company and with his encouragement, it is possible to be both sensible and optimistic—in the same breath!

† † †

Next, you adopt a general stance of cautious optimism, knowing that the problem is serious but not knowing all the specifics. Fortunately, the process throughout the year turns out to be quite simple. You take two doses of medicine per week, and this schedule is set in the first month of work with Dr. R. The process does not vary after that. Blood tests are taken at two-week intervals; at the end of a year, you are reporting to the tumor clinic for examinations at two-month intervals. Twice during the first year you have X rays and proctoscopic intestinal examinations, along with regular general physicals.

† † †

During a regular checkup with your family physician, you ask that he examine a rough-skin spot on your wrist. After scrutinizing it, he says, "Mrs. Turnage, I'm afraid to do anything about that; it might be related to your problem."

Six months after the operations, Dr. M says, "Your X rays have changed. There's a spot near your sternum. You need to talk with Dr. R about it."

At the close of a checkup with Dr. R, after X rays, Anne, you mention a soreness in your left shoulder. He reports, "You have an [unknown polysyllabic adjective] condition there." Seeing your mystified look, he quickly adds, "That's arthritis. If it continues, we can give you a shot that will give relief. Why don't you take some aspirin and see if it'll go away."

† † †

You find that the cancer patient has to learn to cut through—or muddle through—the medical mystique.

You rely on the competence of the specialists. You are thankful for

45

NOW, GOD,
while we are getting ready
for a checkup,
we feel
the tensions building.

Keep us from panic.

Make us serene.

Give us good news.

If we don't get good news,
give us
the kinds of
strength we need
to cope
with bad news.

Help us see that
setbacks are not defeat,
new situations call for
new determination—
not giving up.

LOOK, GOD,
cancer is rampant
in our families and
all over the place.

We don't like
this situation,
and
You don't either.

Our prayers are
for people
involved in research,
for those who
treat cancer patients,
for those who
stand by them,
and for the
patients themselves.

Work, we ask,
through all these,
to dispose of this
disease.

the skills and knowledge of the surgeon; you are glad about the cautious honesty he practices. Early, you realize that he does not encourage you to build up foolish expectations. On the other hand, you have to interpret his personal reactions. He is uncomfortable with emotions; you cannot expect the skilled surgeon also to be an expert counselor. You can detect his concern, even though he has difficulty sending out signals. You read his restraint as a result not only of his scientific caution and accuracy but also as a protection against emotional complications.

When Dr. M says, "You're doing as well as can be expected at this point," you are ready to set off fireworks. When he releases you from the hospital a day or two ahead of his prediction, you take it as an occasion for wild celebration. When he states that he avoids making firm forecasts, you realize that your problem is serious—without his having to tell you that you had better "get your affairs in order."

During this year, you tell Dr. R about your brother-in-law's experience after surgery for melanoma seven years ago. When a new growth had to be removed, Baker was told to "get his affairs in order." Dr. R states, "Doctors don't have to use phrases like that. It's better to say, 'You have a serious problem, but we're going to work with you on it.'" He goes on to explain that growths of this type occur in series. The encouraging fact is that Baker's system has fought off these developments for seven years.

† † †

Your unwritten "contract" with Dr. R calls for him to worry about the technical details without your knowing all the facts. For instance, in the regular checkups, he often tells you that the reports from the blood tests are "beautiful." A word like "asymptomatic" becomes melodious. You are confident that he is keeping up with the records, that he

46

and his staff are working with facts even though you are not familiar with them. After the blood tests are taken, the agreement is that he will call before five o'clock if the reports reveal significant features that you need to know or if the dosage of medicine needs to be changed.

The medical and technical procedures constitute a strange, frightening world. You work on skills in handling your end of the process. Each time, you feel mild tension as you await telephone calls (none has ever been necessary) on days when blood tests are taken. Your anxiety mounts each time you go for a checkup to the surgeon or to the tumor clinic. During the days leading up to each exam, minor discomforts or routine difficulties take on enormous proportions; irritation and fretfulness expand; psychologically, life pushes itself up to the edge of death again. Memories of the initial crisis rise again and lurk in normal shadows.

Each visit to the clinic in the first year brings assurance that "things are going well." You therefore leave each examination in a festive mood. The release almost makes the preparatory anxiety worthwhile. Skies grow brighter, grins break out, laughter spouts easily. People who ask to be informed become sounding boards and amplifiers for the celebration. In your cautious optimism the caution fades.

You meet the cancer patient's difficulty with the overpowering forces of the medical complex. In hospitals, it takes the form of unexplained regimentation. Patients often feel that they are victims rather than beneficiaries of the process. The medical world is "home" for the professionals, but it is "foreign territory" for patients. You recall a

THANKS A LOT,
GOD:

for that nurse
who brought
your kind of joy
into the room,
without being spooky.

for Your healing hand
working through equipment
as well as people—
their knowledge
skills
kindness.

patient who said she was glad that doctors and nurses are casual, but who also said, "I cannot chat about the weather when I'm being stood on my head and someone is shining a light in my rear."

You find that nurses, for all their skills and concern, are careful not to reveal information which the doctor needs to interpret. Nurses do not choose your treatments or interpret them; they carry out orders and deliver messages. The nurses use practical skills (poker faces, calmness, the routine attitude) in hiding information; the doctors decide whether to communicate information to you and the family. Nurses administer drugs; they are not free to explain what those drugs do. You lecture yourself, saying that the nurses frequently catch it—resistance or defiance from patients who do not understand what is happening to them. Therapists, aides, volunteers also get caught in the cross fire. Eventually, you learn that they work within specific orders and guidelines, often without knowing anything about the patient except that he or she is to get such and such treatment, that he or she occupies a specific bed in a specific room.

But medical personnel also hand you bundles of cheer. Care and efficiency are necessary; cheerfulness is a luxury in the medical world. However, it becomes an essential diversion for the patient and an antidote to resignation, bitterness, or discouragement. One practitioner of cheerful and attentive care is nurse V. An elder in a Presbyterian church, she regards her work as ministry to the patient and the family, although she does not play chaplain. Without abandoning her professional role, she brings personal warmth into the scene. Without being a comedienne, she finds laughter at surprising spots. Without breaking rules, she offers friendship as well as care.

† † †

You are impressed that this human quality can operate in clinics or offices too. A physician says, "I don't ask a patient, 'Why do you hurt?' I leave myself open to these complaints, but the general attitude is an expectation that things are better and that you are going to succeed. It's not just hoping; it's an affirmation in the immediate as well as in the distant future."

You admire the mood that prevails throughout the staff of the tumor clinic. Nurses and technicians give the impression that you patients are members of a winning team. For instance, when worry prompts you to call, the medical technician P accepts the calls as routine. She is quick to reassure you, "I'll be glad to have the doctor call you, but I'm sure you have nothing to worry about. If there had been a problem with the X ray, he would've let you know right away." This assurance is even more potent than cheerfulness, but you get both assurance and cheerfulness in generous proportions from personnel in the clinic. D and A, the nurses on duty there, are quick to notice improvements and to congratulate patients. You overhear D say to a frail older patient, "Look at that! You've gained a pound since you were here last. And you're looking so well." This too is practice of the healing art, particularly to patients whose ailments are discouraging.

I know what you are going through because I have been there and I know that love and support are as important as medical skills and chemotherapy and X rays. Our thoughts are with you and our prayers are for you.

B.H.

† † †

Through this year, you notice that, for all their knowledge and skills and for all their devotion to improving the human lot, medical personnel are not superhuman. They too make mistakes; they too are limited in their

49

knowledge and in their ability to communicate. In other words, the cancer patient and the family of the cancer patient do well to develop skills at understanding. Some ask for detailed information; you put yourselves in the group who choose to live with limited access to information. Some find it easy to trust their physicians; others move in tension with and mistrust the medical profession. Your pattern has been to rely heavily on the professionals for what they offer and to limit your concerns to items which they voluntarily share with you.

Before this illness, you often discussed your conviction that all healing comes from God. You confirmed the belief in private and group study—not only as a sound concept but also as a useful idea for patients and physicians. Now, you are more convinced than ever that the conviction is valid. You benefit from the technical expertise of the medical profession. You have your spirits lifted by professionals and also by the simple people involved in the ministry of healing. You find that the desire to help people to good health and to wholesome living cuts across sectarian lines. You neither condemn nor endorse the extreme practices of faith healing in the sects or in "mainline denominations." You are thankful to the Great Physician for working through scientists and researchers, through doctors and nurses, through administrators and technicians, through prayer and prescriptions.

You are also aware that you are indebted to other people, outside these special groups, for the effects of their prayers. You are glad to have benefited from all these channels of divine healing. You delight in the fact that God desires rich, wholesome life for all. You find this desire of His working through people in a variety of ways—the

You develop a series of "patient practices" to guide your behavior and your attitudes:

1. You will regard your physician and his associates as your companions while you work together to improve your health.

2. You will try not to worry about matters which you cannot control or matters which the physician is better equipped to handle.

3. You will ask questions freely and will expect the physician to reveal information that you need to know.

4. You will make efforts to understand medical terminology; you will ask for explanations when you are confused or do not understand.

5. You will regard medical personnel as caring human beings; you will not regard them as superhumans who can perform miracles on demand, or as arch-villains who intend to mistreat or neglect patients.

6. You will respect the differences between the professional and the lay person, between the generalist and the specialist.

7. You will cooperate with prescribed procedures and will expect to understand them as fully as possible.

8. You will be living with uncertainty; so will the experts.

9. You will regard yourself as an agent in the healing process rather than a victim of disease.

10. You will see health as a gift from God, given through many channels.

11. You will, if necessary, try new drugs or experimental programs—not only to help yourself but also to help others.

12. You are not alone; your triumphs or disasters can give meaning to this disease if, through you, information can be gained to help others.

research team that knows how mysteriously intertwined are all the factors that make for health, the quiet unassuming persons in service roles who sense that their mood affects the healing process, the fellow patients who inspire determination by their example and by their concern, the friends and associates who provide forms of strength-courage-determination not available through other channels, the tough-minded physicians or patients whose discipline allows them to confront limitations and to live victoriously within them, the people who have time to listen and to interpret from outside so that fresh power flows in.

These forces, officially or unofficially parts of the healing process, are channels of divine energy.

And so are you!

4

Leaning on Family and Friends

THROUGH YOUR INITIAL daze, Mac, B-R plays a major role in listening as you talk about the trauma you and the family are going through. In one of these conversations, as you are describing the kind of help people are providing, he observes that the body of people who care is reacting like a physical body fighting off infection or pain. "The whole organism orients itself to the part that hurts. Isn't it the circulatory system that sends the right kind of corpuscles to the infected area? The community of concern—here and elsewhere—is focusing its healing attention on Anne and your family."

When Shaw was in kindergarten, one of his favorite Sunday school teachers was H-S, a Japanese lady who studied hospital administration in the United States. While you are still in the hospital, she calls from Tokyo to express her concern and to find out about your progress. Her call comes while Shaw is dressing for the day. He gets the "treat" of renewed contact with his friend and of talking with her across the Pacific.

F and P, who "sat" with your children while you were in Texas for a weekend early in January, schedule a spaghetti supper as their contribution to your family's diet, the week after your release from the hospital. Earlier, F had also sent to the hospital a carefully selected novel which she had enjoyed and which she thought would provide you with a suitable, sentimental diversion. The spaghetti supper is generous in proportions; your family, including Grandmother Shaw now, insists that F and P both stay to enjoy the meal. The food brings nourishment; the companionship becomes another source of energy and renewal.

You cannot name all the attentions to the patient and the family during those first three weeks or during this whole year: books, gifts, flowers, visits, notes, offers, calls, food, messages, prayers. You are impressed with the concern and with the creative expressions of that concern. People respect the family's need for privacy; and they are skillful with concrete, helpful gestures. For you, these expressions have an almost sacramental meaning. Other people are sharing your burdens so that your load is easier—at a very practical level. You see this aid as another healing force; it helps your physical recovery, and it also strengthens all of you to cope with life—on the basis of a new, miserable reality with which you are going to live and on the basis of a new, lively awareness of community.

In April, following your surgery in January, the mother of Lynn's friend M dies, two weeks after exploratory surgery for cancer. Another young friend, C, is collaborating with Lynn to think of ways to help M during her family's distress. C calls you, Anne, to ask, "Since you all have been through a painful experience recently, I thought that you and Lynn and I could figure out how we can help M and her family now."

† † †

A fresh friendship develops for Neil through the spring. G, a classmate in high school and the son of neighbors who are longtime friends, issues several invitations for Neil to go bowling. The two boys play basketball together. At the same time, G's younger brother watches for chances to befriend Shaw Turnage.

† † †

Shaw's friend R and his family graciously include Shaw in family excursions while Anne is recuperating. Naturally a social being, Shaw—because of this generosity—does not have to make drastic changes in his life-style during the crisis. His social needs are being met by thoughtful friends and their thoughtful parents. R's mother leaves a standing invitation for Shaw to visit R after school whenever this arrangement will help.

† † †

The new spring term in school and your new course with a group of graduating students becomes another channel of therapy. The wife of one of the students sends one of your favorite desserts with a note that reads, "Cake baking is not one of my special abilities, but W and I hope this will help you and the kids."

On the athletic field, Shaw and Neil are encouraged to participate

55

PLEASE GOD,
don't let this ordeal
damage
our children.

Develop resilience
in them
so that
they can bounce back
from this jolt.

Give them strength
for these days,
so that
they can look back
at this time
as a time
when they became
stronger people.

Put love and faith
in them
so that
the pain and strength
will come out as
gentleness.

fully. Athletics becomes another area in which the students practice kindness.

You Turnages are able to shift gears from the "emergency" psychology to "redeeming the routine." Students who helped with the move from hospital to home quickly become more casual and more general in their support.

You are impressed at the ability of people to sense appropriate action at different stages and for different persons. For instance, a number of close friends do not come to visit. They convey their concern by telephone calls, by notes and messages. The Cs in Nashville and the Ms in Austin along with other friends-at-a-distance stay in close touch by telephone calls, each a morale boost.

At another level, B and T and their tiny daughter W come for an overnight visit within the first month. The A family arranges a free weekend so that they can visit, to convince themselves that your condition is progressing satisfactorily and to refresh old ties of friendship.

Locally, Grandmother Shaw prepared to "bar the door" to visitors so that you can get the required rest. Friends see to it that she is not confined by this routine assignment, that she has visitors to chat with and luncheon invitations to brighten her time.

Throughout this first year, you learn to admit that you are living on the receiving end. Your usual orientation calls for you to take initiatives, to provide service, to be givers. Here, during this year, you are forced to acknowledge your dependence on the generosity of others. In early childhood, you were taught that it is "more blessed to give than to receive." You are discovering that giving is also *easier* than receiving. You have to find new bearings; instead of trying to be gracious givers, you are learning to be gracious in receiving, to be gladly dependent on other people.

You begin to see this personal attention from other people as a channel through which the necessary grace of God enters your scene.

While you are developing these required skills, you are also learning that the receiver can make life easier or more difficult for the person who gives. Beyond gratitude, there is the possibility of two-way sharing. The thoughtful people who reach out to you are gifts from God; so are the services and things they bring. As receivers, you open up your lives to them—admitting your needy condition and permitting them to share their strengths. As this goes on, all of you learn that situations can change abruptly and the roles can shift drastically. You accept the gifts as coming not only from the person who delivers them but also from the Giver of all good gifts. You even accept the fact that you have to have His gifts in the form of "their" gifts.

Personal help comes through casseroles, checks, cakes—realities that convey love. Some provide essentials; some pay bills and bring beauty or diversion; some maintain or enrich living; others add convenience or bright trimmings.

I have seldom seen such a spontaneous "uprising" of affection and concern as occurred with the news of Anne's illness. Everyone participated in it somehow, and knew other people shared in a kind of community emotion. Surely you must have felt that ... And I hope you know I "participated" too, that my love and support are a part of all that surrounds you.

S.L.

† † †

57

GOOD GOD,
We marvel that
Your love is reflected
so forcefully
in the human concern
we receive:
the teenagers who
fixed a special supper
for our family,
the kind neighbor
who took care of our kids,
the casual acquaintance
whose inquiries were more
than casual.

Thanks for the network of
care that communicates
Your love to us
and to them.

AMEN.

Over the long haul, beyond the first few weeks, you are amazed and grateful for continuing concern from people. Grandmother Shaw is able to stay for several weeks. J and J come by frequently for cheerful—always brief—visits that brighten the days. R and F are always ready to share encouragement, conversation, diversion, or weeping. At one point, Mac says to them, "I need to talk with someone who knows that there's not much difference between laughing and weeping and praying." R's prompt reply is, "I find no difference at all." People at work offer constructive encouragement. Administrators at school encourage you, Mac, to pick up your teaching responsibilities and to start a new course while Anne is still in the hospital; they state that you can call in whatever resource persons you need in order to develop the course.

Gifts of money seem to arrive at the right moment, not only to pay bills but also to boost morale. These gifts enable the family to employ household help one day a week while Anne is regaining her strength.

S, in a telephone conversation months after the operation, says, "We do not say this to you often, but there are a lot of us who continue to keep you close in our prayers."

Your secretary W and her husband A bring in a lavish meal in the first weeks after your operation. They continue through the year—along with many others—to share the rhythm of celebration at good news, anxiety buildups before each examination. Their steady care pumps power into your whole family.

L brings a plant on the anniversary of your surgery, saying, "I had to get something for you that is living, to celebrate this first anniversary."

† † †

Soon after the first interview with Dr. R, you send out a mimeographed letter to your usual Christmas card list. The effort is therapeutic in several ways. For one thing, you failed to send a Christmas greeting, so there is some therapeutic value in "catching up." The letter is also a quick way of responding appreciatively to people who contacted you and to whom you have not responded by notes. More important, through the letter you interpret the situation while you are releasing a call to prayer. You contact people from whom you heard and others who had not heard about your emergency. You retell the events briefly, try to help the readers join in your affirmations, and invite them to rally their prayers:

We will continue to pray for a miracle to match the recovery already given; and we pray for strength-courage-wisdom-faith for whatever the future holds. And that is where you continue to fit in. We have been overwhelmed by the concern which has been expressed. In fact, we have discovered afresh what we have often talked about, what we have known all along—that we are dependent on the power of love to sustain and heal. Your notes-calls-gifts-words-prayers have been beautiful evidence of God's healing power. Through you and your love, channels of divine energy have been flowing into us. We are grateful to you and for you. The community here has been beautifully supportive and helpful practically. . . . Another dimension of this experience has been confirmation of our conviction that life itself is a gift and we cannot afford to take it for granted. . . .

† † †

The family attacks routine household chores with less reluctance; the children take on additional responsibilities without apparent resentment. Complaints, occasionally; resentment, not obviously. As parents, you regard the new skills as suitable training for the children's future homemaking—sorting dark from light clothes *en route* to the

59

washing machine, mending and maintaining their favorite garments, sweeping and mopping and vacuuming, loading and unloading the dishwasher. Eight-year-old Shaw requests that he be given more important jobs than simply taking out the trash; he also wants other members of the family to take their turns with the trash detail. The three probably do not realize how much healing is in their work and their sensitivity.

† † †

A distant relative, who intends to be helpful, in a long-distance call quizzes you, "What have you done to prepare the children for the jolt they'll have? Are you and they going to be ready when the time comes?" You respond that you are trying to take an optimistic view of the future and that the children are aware of the uncertainties ahead. You also explain that you do not intend to borrow unnecessary trouble from the future. You get the message that your caller does not regard this as an adequate response. Clearly, he regards you as naive if not foolish. The conversation ends after you ask whether he called to let you cheer him up.

> We pray that god may give you all the strength and courage to face the days ahead and that there may be others near you to give you friendship, love, and concern.
>
> E. and B.N.

On the other hand, you discover that once you convey hope and trust, with suitable realism, other people become more confident and can express their feelings more openly. One letter reads, "Now that we have received signals that you are celebrating in the face of this difficulty, it is easier for us to enter in. We can celebrate life with you, even while we are worried about you."

In other words, you discover that you, as the focus of people's attention, help shape how your family and friends respond. And you discover that the best way for you to relate to them is in openness and with full descriptions of your physical and emotional scene.

† † †

You recall, from your study of Japanese social structures, that their society can be described as a web of forces. Individuals and institutions operate in such a way that when relationships are strained, they pull to help hold people up and knit society into a unit. In relationships with other figures, some authoritative and some collegial, individuals are able to keep their balance.

Your year's experience with cancer helps you to see your own scene in terms of a network of powerful concern. The system works in such a way that, when one point droops, the surrounding forces exert extra strain to uphold the sagging point in the network.

At church one Sunday, a casual acquaintance stops you, Anne, to say, "We keep on praying for you, and you appear to be doing quite well. We'll continue our prayers for you."

Toward the end of the year, a letter arrives from R-H, a German missionary in Tokyo: "I am grateful to have your letter and to know how you are doing. Now, my prayers for you can be more specific."

Shortly after returning home from the hospital, you receive a call from McG, a fellow graduate student in earlier days: "I want to know how you're doing, so I can pass information along to our friends and so that all of us can 'pull for you' properly."

† † †

As old ties are re-formed, you realize that ties from the past and ties with distant places have become part of you. In the new significance of

61

old relationships, you begin to see that you have been walking on holy ground wherever you have been.

H and N and their family were your close friends when you lived in Texas. A few months before your surgery, they were vacation guests in your home. During this reunion, both couples tried to articulate the value of your companionship through the years. You had to give up the effort because the sentiments were too strong. Through his company's communication system, during slack times, H calls for reports. During your hospitalization, his calls come daily to Mac's office; H relays reports to other friends in Texas. Throughout the year, he continues to make contacts after each of your major checkups.

Of course, you are thankful for H's own personal concern; you are aware that he represents concern that surrrounds you. He becomes an important symbol of "the network."

He also articulates the community's conviction about the power of intercessory prayer when he says, "Anne has meant so much to so many of us that we couldn't let anything happen to her."

5

Drawing Strength from Familiar Sources

WHILE YOU ARE moving through this year, you are exploring your past, finding out what makes you tick, reviewing the forces that have shaped you.

You discover, at the core of your consciousness, a tangle of convictions, memories, rejected-and-absorbed influences, sparks that have been struck by personalities you encountered along the way.

† † †

You feel the subtle and not-so-subtle effects of the families in which you grew up. In retrospect, you appreciate your parents' hardheaded realism—partly the product of Depression experience, partly the result of Bible-Belt piety, partly the product of their highly personal commitments. Accidentally and intentionally, they conveyed to you both the good and the bad of the "Protestant work ethic."

Limited in education but long on determination, they knew how to shape life as it came. They faced difficulties without whimpering;

And what is faith?

Faith gives substance
to our hopes,
and makes us certain
of realities
we do not see.

HEBREWS 11:1 (N.E.B.)

Can you rely on a
MIRACLE
while it's happening?
...when you can't see it?

they built life-styles that were dictated by circumstances and that were becoming to their personalities. You wonder what elements from their patterns you have adopted. You are grateful for their toughness and tenderness, transplanted in you.

† † †

You realize during this year that old familiar convictions become sources of new strength and life, foundations under your insecurity. You develop your own restatements of tired, valued certainties:

—God built people so that they are equipped to live under his control and in lively companionship with him.

—People are both fragile and magnificent, corrupt and beautiful.

—God's cleansing, powerful love reshapes and reclaims both personal and public life.

—God has worked through the generations to establish control over his whole world, by seizing particular persons and particular groups; then he has set them into motion for the benefit of his whole creation.

—Jesus brought God and people together; he embodied God's brand of love in the arena of human life.

—God commissions his committed followers to share their disciple-role with the whole human race.

—It is impossible to separate the physical from the spiritual, the secular from the sacred.

—All people are objects of God's love; they deserve respect and they need various forms of help—encouragement, correction, instruction, liberation.

—Whether or not he is acknowledged by the human agents involved, God is at work wherever joy, hope, peace are discovered and practiced and shared.

—Jesus the Christ brought into focus both God's love and humanity's potential.

—He is working to conquer evil wherever it exists—in human bodies, in institutions, in international relations, in social life.

—He binds contaminated people into holy alliances, for their benefit and for the benefit of all people.

—The life he gives is rich life, here and now, within the restrictions of human existence—not only "out there" beyond the present limitations.

—Death can be confronted without panic, because in the resurrection of Jesus God demonstrated his mastery of all foes—including pain, sorrow, misery, death.

—We are living in the time when God's people discover their true nature and function by sharing their experience of his grace—until he finishes up the job in his own way and at his own time.

—All human relations (including friendship, marriage, family) are filled with promise, because they can reflect the kind of love which God invested in humanity as he lived among us in the person of Jesus.

—Our glorious opportunity (not oppressive duty) is to be witnesses to and practitioners of God's love in all aspects of life.

—One way to give people a chance at richer life is to expect the best of them.

While you are formulating these statements of belief, you are also seeing that you stack them differently at different times. In one incident, your convictions about people rise to the top; at other times, you reach for the convictions that assure you of God's love—or that push you to get to work.

You move on through the year—reworking, remodeling, expanding, and correcting these statements—with new antennae for detecting experiences, past and present, that reinforce or reshape your convictions. You see the bundle of statements not as a burden but as a source of energy and as guidelines for your journey.

You remember inspirational youth conferences where you lighted your share of candles beside lakes. You are products of the church's ministry to and with youth. The church has been a shaping force for you, the church with all its weaknesses and all its glories.

You are glad that the church opened windows from narrow parochialism to a larger world, stimulated your social consciences, enabled you to see yourselves as agents for justice, influenced you to be dissatisfied with conditions as they are, and taught you to regard yourselves with respect. The church commissioned you to share what you learn, to correct situations that need change, and to stand up under pressure.

† † †

On Maundy Thursday, as part of your responsibility as an elder in the church, Anne, you plan with some other people the "first communion" of a group of teenagers who are completing their confirmation training.

This event becomes more significant than you had expected; it is the first communion service for you since your surgery. Your prayers, during the periods of silence, request strength for the newly confirmed members and for all people who have ailments. You are thankful for the larger comradeship, symbolized in those who gather at the table, which has been holding you up and holding you together. And you are glad to be a part of the progression through history of those who find their resources, their understandings, and their missions in the events memorialized in eucharist. Again, in solemn joy, you Turnages are celebrating life.

† † †

You also recall powerfully shaping events that have occurred around you in the past.

On the day their three children died in a fire, D and R told you and others, "We know what a temptation bitterness can be, but we think we've already turned that corner." Later, they managed to rebuild, with each other and with their son who survived the tragedy. They also invented ways to make suitable connections with other youngsters. They presented a copy of *The New English Bible* to each child in the Sunday church school, as memorial gifts honoring their own children.

A and V had keen appreciation for music of all styles. When V died, A requested that the "Hallelujah Chorus" be played as the funeral recessional, an appropriate expression of their attitudes about life and death.

At the time of their retirement, Grandmother and Grandfather Shaw demonstrated the kind of flexibility you hope to practice. They moved from a town in the deep South, where the population had never exceeded 3,000, to the West Coast where their church counted over 5,000 members and where they designed new patterns for themselves.

Seven years after she was widowed, Grandmother Turnage lost her home, along with the whole neighborhood, in a hurricane on the Gulf Coast. Within a week after the storm she was negotiating the purchase of a smaller place in a new location, starting over at the age of sixty-nine.

> I had to do something that would relieve my pain and join with you in a song of hope. I took my camera and went to the park to look for signs of spring. Maple buds, a butterfly, and a crocus caught my eye and got caught on my film. Enjoy these for what those moments meant to me as well as whatever pleasure you may get from them yourself. You know I love you and that love is being used for your life.
>
> P.C.

This review helps you see that you have both resources and examples to use in coping with your problems, in adjusting to new situations, and in moving ahead into new stages of life.

People around you have put flesh onto the faith, and you have derived benefits from their lives. Now you want your living to convey and embody the same kind of victory.

† † †

Within a few months after your surgery, the two of you are invited to write a week's series of meditations for your denomination's guide for personal and family worship. You accept the assignment, as you have on previous occasions. You compose the work and turn it in to the editor. You hardly think about this task again until—months later—the series appears in print.

Now, you begin to receive notes thanking you for the meditations and prayers you composed; the notes become corrective encouragement and reassurance as you are building up tensions. The notes arrive while you are preparing for extensive tests. The writing started out as a simple project; responses to your work become reminders of power available.

> We bombard the gates of heaven that His healing power may be unloosed. You both mean so much to us. We are confident that His presence is real to you now perhaps as never before.
>
> T. and F. K.

† † †

You learn again that life is curiously woven, that continuity and abrupt disruptions are both patterns in the fabric. When difficulties arise, you gain strength from remembering that you survived the trauma at the beginning of the year.

A friend observes, "At least, as you meet problems in the future, you will be able to look back on this period and say, 'We made it through *that*, so we can keep going now.'"

When you cope with serious problems, you now see that you are handling ultimates. You detect that the difference between your present and past situations is a difference of intensity. You are dealing with more serious illness than you have met before; you are turning to spiritual resources with more intense hunger than you ever felt before. With the intense pain, intense delights grow. The importance of everything is magnified. When you are simply tired, it feels like exhaustion; when you learn a lesson, it changes your life; when you wrestle with realities, you are in a life-or-death struggle; when you are with your family, a routine meal becomes a banquet.

Not all the discoveries are pleasant. When you face strains in your church life, you become impatient with trivia. Your feelings are more easily outraged; your worries more readily lead you astray; your imaginings more easily move into gloom. As you meet and admit these difficulties, you remind yourselves that a Power greater than yours has coped with greater problems than these—even in your own recent past.

You are recognizing that life is essentially mysterious. You are accepting the confusing parts of the mystery at the same time you are affirming solid realities. But you now know that mystery does not have to terrify. When mystery produces pleasure, you label it "surprise"; when mystery produces pain, you label it "tragedy." Maybe you are developing a maturity that will allow you to embrace the mystery without feeling that you have to attach labels to its details or unravel its riddles. You face uncertainties about the future, whether you live or die, whether the present shape of life continues for a long time or a short, whether you can understand or not. And, in the face of all these uncertainties, you have enough strength, courage, help,

LORD,

*While
we are dealing
with this new misery,
help us to
find new ways to
celebrate.*

*We want to shout,
even
while we are in trouble,
that You are the One
who keeps us going.*

*We want to sing
when the situation
calls for sighing,
to laugh
when tears are expected,
to proclaim
when groaning
comes natural.*

...a thorn was given me
in the flesh....

Three times I besought
the Lord about this,
that it should leave me;
but he said to me,

"My grace is sufficient
for you,
for my power is made perfect
in weakness."

2 Corinthians 12:7–9 (RSV)

Paul knew (and we know)
what (and we know) we need is

GOD'S GRACE
—to get rid of a problem
or to live ~~with~~ on top of it

truth, light, joy—enough to go on living and loving today, and through however many tomorrows you are given.

† † †

While reaching back to find resources for living in crisis, you are learning to live with a series of remodeled convictions and with a large crop of questions. You are learning to choose and shape your memories so that they refresh you in the present and fortify you for an unknown future. You are learning to move ahead, with imposed restraints, to share what you are learning. And you are living fully, within the restrictions.

> You continue with "You don't know, . . . but you do know. . . ."
>
> You don't know what the future holds, but you do know that you have been cared for and that you are in God's hands now.
>
> You do not know precise information about all the physical realities; you do know that cancer is a formidable foe and that you have resources to use in the conflict.
>
> You do not know how long life will last; you do know that there is work worth doing and energy supplied for doing it.
>
> You do not know what battles you will have to fight; you do know that you will not have to battle alone, you will have the support of scientific knowledge, human companionship, and divine power.
>
> You do not know what your personal future will be—either in extent or quality; you do know that you can trust Him.

6

Returning to Routine

YOU WONDER WHETHER and when and how life can get back to normal after a trauma like yours.

Will you ever again be looked at as a person, or will you forever be labeled "the lady with cancer"?

Can you handle the responsibilities that were your lifeblood—in your family, with your church, in the community?

Will other people let you back in or will they push you off, put you on a shelf?

Can you cope with pity—with being the center of attention, with being a project for people to help?

Can you and your family make the adjustments to a life-style that is both different and necessary?

† † †

You are delighted to get out of the hospital, and the family is delighted to be reunited under the same roof. You realize that you still need to be protected from strains. You notice that Mac handles most of the telephone conversations, particularly those that might subject you to pressures. When he senses that a call will give you strength (instead of

75

So
do not be anxious
about tomorrow;
tomorrow
will look after itself.

Each day
has troubles enough
of its own.

MATTHEW 6:34 (N.E.B.)

TODAY
let's celebrate
the JOYS
that are
HERE NOW!✳

NEVER mind
the anxieties
that may
or may not
come LATER

drain your strength), he hands you the telephone. Grandmother Shaw takes care of visitors in the living room, when she detects that you have had enough company.

Then, the first occasion arises when no one else is there to answer the telephone's ring. You take it yourself, and you are on your own. Providentially, the caller is a friend who knows how to convey cheer.

You are getting back to normal! You answered the telephone!

Mac, I am a great sitter. After time goes by (and you think best) I would be happy to stay a night or part of the night at the hospital — on a regular basis, with your wife, if this will be any help to you.

J.B.

† † †

At your first interview, the cancer specialist advises you to think of yourself as normal and take up regular routine as soon as you are able.

On the way home from the clinic, you two talk about the days ahead. You plan (with only a slight nod at the possibility of its not working out) to meet a long-standing commitment, scheduled for six weeks after your operation. You do not need to cancel those plans! You are moving back toward your regular operation. (And now, you do not have to think of surgery *every* time you use the word operation.)

† † †

Through the spring and summer you set goals, and the goals themselves are therapy. The two of you accept separate invitations to training events that will involve absences from home for a week on one occasion and for three weeks on another. You, Anne, will spend a week in Texas training as a consultant on teaching adults in the church. You, Mac, will spend three weeks in special, intensive

78

training to improve your skill in the classroom. You realize that the separations, when life together has become more precious, will be difficult; but you decide to make the leap of faith as a way of confirming your new health.

You are grateful for the way friends and neighbors help the family during the crisis. Food is stocked in the freezer; entire meals are brought in. The food is delicious and the care is welcome.

You are even more grateful when you are able to help the family prepare its own meals. You ease through the steps: suggesting items that need to be purchased at the grocery store; then, deciding on menus and coaching the teenagers while they do the cooking. Later, you move to the kitchen as director of activities, seated on a kitchen stool in the happy center of confusion. Finally, you feel like declaring a national holiday when you are able to plan and prepare a meal for the family.

You become aware of the validity of diversion. A young friend lends you her copy of a lovely romantic novel that she enjoyed and that she thinks you will like.

The first time you get fully dressed after your return home from the hospital is for a "luncheon out." M invites you and Grandmother Shaw to celebrate your recovery with an outing to a neighborhood restaurant.

The ordinary scene glows with glamor.

O, GOD,
we have benefited
from the ministry
of other people
who have to
confront and conquer
difficulties.

We ourselves
have encountered
trouble before.

Now
we need to
focus our attention
not on
the difficulties
but on
being productive.

Help us
turn this corner sensibly,
so
we can pick up
our tasks
gracefully.

You find that there is also a legitimate place for emotional release.

Calls from friends become occasions for special memories. R and P, from whom you have not heard in several years, state that your friendship has been a shaping force in their lives and in the life of their young family. Your love for them and the fresh contact washes your psyche with tears.

You discover that tears also contain joy. You are delighted that you are on hand to participate in Lynn's final year of high school with all of its excitement.

Your delight with life is intensified by the keen sense that you might have missed some of these chapters.

You know intellectually what you have been going through, but the emotional upheaval continues. You are surprised that tears flow more openly, that laughter comes more quickly, that beauty around you is breathtaking, that people and their concerns are more obvious and more important.

† † †

A month late, but you are able to handle it! Postponed because of your illness, a farewell dinner in your home honors a colleague and his wife. The four guests are a bit ill at ease; they are afraid you are "overdoing."

But the hostess role is one you enjoy; these two couples know that you want to be in that role. You do not want to cut back on the quality of hospitality you offer. The meal is lavish. The guests forget that you are a cancer patient. You yourself even forget a bit. The friends and the occasion are the center of attention.

> We can only offer our love and prayers. The day we got the news about Anne I called everbody I knew, then I had to do something, so I walked … when I got back, I called Ruth and she said she had just waxed all her floors that did not need waxing. Now this crazy activity did not help Anne at all. But we were so distressed. We love you very much, Anne, and pray God will heal you. We pray for the big miracle.
>
> B.S.

You are returning to normal. You are taking up the activities that make your life distinctive.

† † †

Now that you have been seriously ill, you meet the question, "How are you?" with new responses. It is no longer a casual greeting; you sense that people really want to know particulars. And you want them to know your good news; you want them to be at least as comfortable as you are with the realities. Therefore, you learn to answer with personalized, scientific information instead of generalized pleasantries.

"Fine. I had a good report last week at my regular checkup, so we have a great deal to be thankful for."

"I feel great. I'm having no complications from the chemotherapy; we still rely on the prayers and concerns of other people—and on the medical help."

Our prayers have been with you continuously since we learned of your distress and operation. I know God has sustained your family as well as your surgeon and physician. May you heal and be whole again.

J.S.

† † †

In you, routine is operating as a healing power. You see signals that recovery is under way when you are able to pick up your normal activities again. The act of moving back to normal becomes therapy. You do not know whether you have strength until a task demands it of you. Then, your exercise produces greater strength and enables you to move ahead.

For instance, you want to meet the commitments for the spring which you made before your operation. You let the plans stand, hoping that you will be able to measure up. The plans themselves give you something to look forward to, even though there is doubt about whether you can handle the load. As you pick up steam and move into the regular program, you have the necessary stamina. There is a boomerang effect: the commitment produces anticipation and eagerness; the anticipation and eagerness become healing forces. Your strength improves. As you put that energy to work, you discover that you are able to function normally in normal situations.

Surprise! You are on the road to recovery and the route is through routine.

7

Reaching Out to Other People

"THEY" ARE SURE that you have something to offer their friend T. At church, a fellow elder mentions that T, the wife of another elder, is to have exploratory surgery for suspected cancer. With your operation nine months in the past and with your children the same age as T's, you hope that you can help her and her family in this distress. You learn that she had breast surgery seven years ago and that she has been ill for several weeks.

You hesitate to get involved, to subject yourself to extra emotional pressures. You also feel that you must make contact with T. As you see it, you have no choice in the matter. You have been fortunate in your health since the surgery; your outlook is promising. Hopefully, your presence can help her and her family find the kind of strength you have been given.

While T is in the recovery room, you visit with her husband at the hospital. He says that the operation confirmed the presence of an inoperable malignancy. T will begin chemotherapy immediately.

During the weeks of her hospitalization, you often visit her.

You and T have not been close before these visits, but you and she are able to converse about cancer and about your future. She is discouraged at her "repeat performance." Her anxiety is magnified by

83

When we try
to help other people,
we thank You
for giving us
new strength.

When their news
is not
as good as ours,
we feel
pain.

Our prayers
are for all people
who have ailments,
for Your
healing and loving
power
to work in them.
Use us
in the
healing.

AMEN.

the recent death of one neighbor and the serious illness of another—both cancer patients. The two of you talk about "the epidemic." You also talk about the teenagers in your families and about the possibility of their being damaged by the illness of their mothers. You share viewpoints and insights; you swap tales about how you manage to keep going.

You feel awkward because you want her to find something to look foward to—even if it is a simple thing like going out to dinner or getting back into the household routine. But T does not gain enough strength or confidence to mount even modest campaigns.

Her illness subsides enough for her to return home for two brief intervals, but she does not have strength enough to receive visitors. A well-meaning neighbor suggests to her that she is demon-possessed. Not wanting T to be subjected to this kind of treatment again, the family decides to control visits. Her husband indicates that *you* will be welcome at any time; other visitors wear her down instead of boosting her up.

Knowing that she can concentrate on reading for brief moments, you share several books that have been helpful to you. For the most part, they are diversion-type readings or books of brief prayers. When you write your book on the first year with cancer, you decide, it will be designed to be read in bits and pieces.

T's strength fades; she cannot eat; she reenters the hospital. Within a few weeks, she dies.

You are pleased that T's husband asks the elders to serve as honorary pallbearers at her funeral. Beyond visiting with the grieving family, this ceremonial opportunity gives you a chance to do something constructive. You are amazed at and strengthened by the courage her husband and children display. Their serenity becomes a source of serenity for all of you. They are not trying to hide their emotional upheaval, but they are moving through the necessary activities with a contagious calm.

At the funeral, the minister uses one of the prayers from a book you lent to T. Since you are seated with the honorary pallbearers, Mac is with Lynn as she weeps. She senses some of the pain of T's teenagers, and she goes back through her own emotional pressures of several months ago. All of you Turnages realize in these days that memories bring back emotions; you find that you can expect them to return with frequency. You have to cope with both the recurring memories and the accompanying distress.

As you look back after T's death, you feel a sense of failure; you were not able to give her everything you wanted her to have. But, at the same time, you are glad that you had the opportunity to share with her at a deep level. You and your family are stronger because of this sharing; you hope her family is stronger too. With T, you discussed the realities you were both confronting; you faced them unblinkingly; and you talked about the spiritual resources on which you both relied. Now, you want to shift your gears and reach out to her family. Her husband and her children need friendship while they are rebuilding.

According to statistics, heart disease kills more people than cancer. You wonder when attitudes will catch up with the statistical facts, when the public will rearrange the priorities-for-panic.

Frequent announcements in the media about progress in cancer treatment and research sharpen your hope that discovery of the cure is near. Despite these spasmodic reports, professionals working in the fight against cancer state that public knowledge moves more slowly than medicine's march. Currently, many individual patients are doing better than statistics can show, because the records are still being compiled. In fact, statistical proof of progress requires a heavy accumulation of success before it can outweigh past records. And you wonder whether the scorekeepers will ever be able to convince or counterbalance the emotions.

Through the year, you move out to resist the oppression of cancer and its effects on the family, other patients, the public, and even the medical people.

† † †

You wonder why people have such a hard time when they need to talk about cancer. And you wonder whether, in the past, you allowed other patients to talk openly when you stood outside the reach of the disease. Now, you are seeing the scene from a different angle. Lying in the hospital, you wish that the word *cancer* did not produce such alarm. You know that friends intend to be kind and protective; but too much protection stifles, too much camouflage deceives.

> *Your courage reached out and touched us as it has so often in life, and we join you in the spirit of living ··· The day does not pass that you are not here with me.*
> B.P.

Hospital visitors can only speak of "your condition" or "your problem" or "your misfortune."

During a routine office visit, a family physician speaks of "your larger problem," trying to soften the impact. But you are curious. Is he softening the impact for you or for himself? Maybe he is protecting himself and his patients from panic, and maybe this is his way of coping. Maybe, but artificial, veiled words do not protect either you or him from the realities you confront.

You take up the challenge to speak frankly and directly with high hopes that frankness and directness will be contagious.

You decide to take the initiative, to speak up. You are gambling that other people will be able to take your directness, that they will relax when you "dispel the curse" by saying the word *cancer*. You learn to read your audience, to know whether they can tolerate what you call "bold-faced truth."

Your situation may be unusual; you have not asked for complete detailed clinical reports. You can say that your ailment is cancer, that it is a serious—unpredictable—foe. You state your intention to live as fully as you can for whatever length of time you can and within whatever limits are imposed. You are glad when you get the chance to put all of this into conversations; and you hope your frankness will liberate people to feel comfortable with you, even if they cannot be comfortable with conversation about cancer.

So, you begin to see that the patient has opportunities to reach out to the people around, to set them at ease. You appreciate their risk of awkwardness and pain while they are being kind.

† † †

What surprises life holds for us as it moves along! Some fill us with warmth and security and some scare the socks off us. Perhaps the most interesting are those which do both. We are praying for your complete recovery under the hand of our God who is the source of both healing and love.

R.B.

Particularly in the early part of your first year, you need to hear success stories, and you know you need to hear them. You need Dr. R's word that experimental programs are meeting with success. You need the kind of optimism he conveys when he says, "I am convinced that we've had some cases of cure for bowel cancer, but the people haven't lived long enough yet for us to claim statistical success." You feel that you are getting benefits from the latest discoveries when he says, "We now know that you get better results from your medicine if you take it in grape juice rather than citrus juices."

And in turn, through the year, you watch for chances to speak encouraging words to others, from the base of your own good progress and from the base of the work of the clinic.

† † †

You learn, as you move through this first year, that a number of agencies provide aid and encouragement for the cancer patient; many of these agencies are also helping the public to understand and fight cancer.

THE AMERICAN CANCER SOCIETY is the best known of these groups. It is a voluntary organization of over 2,000,000 people and it operates programs of research, education, and service. After M-L had a mastectomy, she insisted on follow-up treatment; the surgeon assured her that she did not need it. Annoyed, M-L asked the local unit of the American Cancer Society to help her. She was referred to the local cancer research facility, where she has frequent checkups and conferences that give her information and confidence. This attention convinces her that her condition is being properly policed, that she is being protected from the danger of undetected complications.

The Society helps patients locate equipment and services they need. It also carries on a program to educate the public, particularly on the value of early treatment. One out of every three cancer patients now recovers; a larger number could be saved by early detection and treatment.

The American Cancer Society sponsors and serves as a clearing house for a number of voluntary groups by which patients help one another. For instance, REACH TO RECOVERY is a rehabilitation program for women who have had breast cancer. Members have had mastectomies; on request, they visit patients while they are recuperating from surgery; the volunteers distribute cheer, literature, exercise equipment, and temporary breast forms.

MAKE TODAY COUNT, a newer group, is publicized as a channel of help for the "terminal cancer patient." Group sessions specialize in information, sharing, and mutual support. F says that he has been given courage to face death openly and constructively because of the comradeship which Make Today Count provides.

OSTOMY brings together cancer patients who have to cope with the inconveniences and indignity of colostomies. H says, "At first the group was shocking to me. They were so frank about the problems that I thought we might get around to comparing scars. Now, I know that the frankness heals; with the group, I learned to talk about my bag without feeling like a freak."

THE LOST CHORD CLUB is a similar association of persons who have had laryngectomies. They and their families help fellow patients as they go through speech retraining. The clubs arrange for speech therapy; and patients and their families gain confidence through sharing experiences with the group.

Another information and service agency, the LEUKEMIA SOCI- ETY OF AMERICA, supports research into causes and cures for leukemia. The society provides information for the public about the disease and its treatment. The national organization conducts an annual financial campaign. Funds are distributed at state and local levels to provide treatment and transportation of patients. Other funds are invested in research on a national and international level. Annually, the Society cosponsors an international symposium, working in cooperation with the World Committee on Comparative Leukemia Research. Local chapters can be contacted through doctors who treat leukemia patients.

Local organizations for the parents of leukemia victims operate

Now to him
who by his power
within us

is able to do far more
than we ever dare to ask
or imagine—

to him be glory

in the Church
through Jesus Christ
for ever and ever,

Amen!

Ephesians 3:20–21 (J. B. Phillips)

He can do more than you
dare to ask...
or dream... or think...
or imagine...
so —
why not ask?

under a variety of labels. Frequently these local organizations are connected with the medical centers which provide treatment and do research. These local groups provide emotional support, conduct discussions, and contribute to research.

CANCER RESEARCH CENTERS, often related to medical schools, are located in major cities. These centers carry on research and offer programs that range from outpatient care to intensive care of the terminally ill. Research grants allow these centers to experiment with promising drugs, to study the complicated psychological and physical effects of the disease, to build new patterns of care for the patient, and to deal with the morale factors. Each center is engaged in specialized projects, and each exchanges discoveries with other centers. As you visit the local center, you find that the program includes counseling, home nurse care, and various other services to improve the quality and extend the length of life.

You also learn that these programs need funds. You decide to mount a quiet campaign to encourage people to make memorial gifts and other contributions to cancer research—particularly through these local centers.

† † †

While you want to reach out to help, you find that you need support in order to function in this capacity. You need help if you are going to give help.

You pull hope out of articles about recent, promising discoveries in cancer research. When you hear that new methods of detection are being developed, you celebrate, dreaming that your children will have a greater chance of avoiding this disaster. When the press reports that new methods of treatment show promise, you wonder eagerly if you will benefit directly from any of the experiments they describe.

You remind yourself and other people that leukemia and Hodgkin's disease are being contained; recent years have brought dramatic success.

Although these bits of public information help, you also need the personal words and spirit that you draw from Dr. R and his reports. He seems always to be enthusiastic about new items of research. He convinces you that your personal progress is great; and he also gets you excited about the future prospects for conquering cancer. In these moments, you draw help from his eagerness; you see that you will get to take advantage of new developments as they occur. You also build your confidence on his statements that whenever he prescribes a medicine or a program, he has several backup options in mind—in case a sequel is needed.

With this kind of stimulation, you can move out more vigorously to offer stimulation and hope to others—about their situations and about your own. In order to convey this hope, you need both information and inspiration. You see that the best form of care flows from one person to another—from doctor to patient, patient to patient, patient to family, family to outsiders.

† † †

Through the year, you try to help people who are indirectly involved with the disease.

As you move toward the summer months, for instance, you discover that your children need assurances about the future, assurances that your family's life can move ahead normally. You take care of this need by aggressive, specific planning for the family's vacation. While the family is caring about you, one of the best things you can do is to help them build confidence.

You have chosen the strategy of "full steam ahead with normal

LOOK, GOD!
now that we are getting
to the end of it,
help us preserve
the values
we have derived
from this first year.

Help us
translate
these values
into permanent
resources.

As we face
the uncertainties
of the future,
keep pushing us
into
rich
new
life.

PLEASE

93

activities" as the best way of meeting your crisis. By this strategy you are able to convince a few. Others continue to worry.

You know that life comes from the hand of God and that it comes in slices and chunks; you do not have to know the shape or dimensions of the whole in order to enjoy the next segment. In other words, you find yourselves trying to make your situation as easy on other people as possible. Sometimes, you speak bluntly about the disease; sometimes you affirm your faith; sometimes you try to convince; sometimes you tell details about your condition or about your reports; sometimes you plunge ahead hoping that your actions will convey proper impressions.

† † †

Also, you feel pressure to reach out purposefully to other cancer patients and their families, although you do not join the official organizations.

At moments, you feel a bit guilty because you are doing well; not all the people you love have this good fortune.

† † †

So, you decide to write this book as a testimony to the fact that it is possible to get through a year with cancer.

And if one year, why not more . . . ?

And if for you, why not for other people . . . ?

8

Wondering Why

As YOU MOVE through the year, the question "Why?" takes odd shapes.

Sometimes, it is a shout of rage, screaming for revenge and release. You hate what is happening and you hate the cancer and you hate its effects on you and on people you love!

At other times, the question is a vague widespread anger—at the medical profession, at people who are healthy, at other patients, at the people who care about you, at the disciplines imposed!

At moments, inarticulate shock becomes whining complaint, while resignation and self-pity whittle away your dignity.

Again, "Why?" is a thin veil over your disappointments. You have assumed that good health is a commodity in permanent supply. Now you are having to readjust, to make room for complications. You want to be a source of strength to your family, not a drain on their strength.

At its best, the question, "Why?" becomes, "What good can result from all this?" "What healthy outcomes can be derived from this illness?"

† † †

You know that the philosophers have worried with the problem of evil for generations.

95

You know that the questioning mind unearths an array of pains. The questions stretch and twist the spectrum of emotions.

You know too that fancy, complex theories have often been reduced to homespun "easy answers."

You do not expect neat, satisfying solutions to the ultimate questions, but you cannot avoid the questions.

So, you still wonder, "Why?"

"You have to take the bitter with the sweet."

Your answer is "I have·to, but I don't like it."

"Every cloud has a silver lining."

You reply, "Why should I have to turn life inside out to find the good in it?"

One theory says that contrast is essential. You cannot appreciate and enjoy the good and beautiful unless they are set against the backdrop of the bad and ugly.

This theory may make sense, but it doesn't make much difference. You can spout these thoughts, but they do not change your feelings or your situation. You live with the notion that life contains a mixture of pain and delight, but the idea does not calm your worries or soothe your discomforts.

So you still wonder "Why?"

"Into each life some rain must fall."

"Just wait. Your turn will come. Sooner or later, every family has to deal with health problems."

In light of your situation, you see this viewpoint as hardheaded realism, but you reserve the right to filter out the gloom which distorts the view. You do not want a mind-set that pours dread over every delight, dampening real though limited joys.

Intellectually, you know you will face restrictions. Human beings are finite; they live in finite settings. Life is a strange mix of joy and sorrow; only the proportions vary within a lifetime. But you do not have to sour your future with doses of dreary fears.

This kind of thinking puts your cautious optimism to the test.

But still you wonder, "Why?"

† † †

"You have to accept the Lord's will."

Thinkers have made a distinction between what God orders and what he permits; they can sort out events coolly with this dividing line. You find little or no satisfaction in this division.

Instead, you choose to put your emphasis on another understanding of the will of God. You are convinced that he chooses to be involved in all the hurts and victories of human life, that he arranges for you and other people to work with him to improve the human situation. With his help, people can be agents for bringing health and wholeness into the human scene. You have experienced the will of God in working with him; you do not want to withdraw, to "accept," to be a mere passenger, impotent and resigned.

Against such fatalists, you argue that it is God's will for you to fight back, to get well, to continue your life and work. You hope you are ready to take whatever comes, but you do have some strong preferences about what comes—and some of those preferences are inspired by God. You want your life to be "in tune" with his will, and you are going to let him know that you have some strong desires about the shape of your future.

Still, you wonder, "Why?"

97

GOD,
we don't understand.

Maybe it wouldn't do us
any good to understand all
the nagging
"Why's."

Focus our attention on the
affirmations we can make—
that you love us,
that we're upheld by your
* power,*
that you're still in control,
that you want us to have full
life.

Then whether we understand
won't matter so much.

† † †

"You reap what you sow."

Although no one has flung this one at you yet, such a cause-and-effect theory often goes unquestioned. Religious training, psychosomatic medicine, cool-headed thinkers, and homemade philosophy have rubbed this notion into the grain.

But you know that any formula is limited in its application; life is more complicated and more personal than any statement about it. Jesus reminded people that rain falls on the just and the unjust alike.

The book of Job defies the simple formula, insisting that some pain is undeserved, some misery is unexplainable. Jesus refused to accept the current assumption that blindness was caused by the sin of the victim or the sin of his forebears.

You have seen bright young lives dimmed by tragedies; you have wept when senseless accidents put abrupt ends to promising futures; you have witnessed the wearing away of clever people by degrading diseases. You cannot believe that simple regulations of justice operate in these patterns.

You affirm that in many areas of human life, the principle of sowing and reaping does apply. But you refuse to accept this principle as adequate to interpret the whole human predicament.

So, still, you wonder, "Why?"

> We just heard of your surgery. This is to say we love you and you are in our prayers constantly. The words are not easy to write but I hope you understand what is in my heart.
>
> B. and E. T.

† † †

"The Devil's after us all. Maybe it's a good thing that we are hearing about demon-possession and exorcism in these troubled times."

98

Your friend T was upset by a visitor who dared her to drive the evil out of her life. No one has thrown this idea at you. (Maybe people are afraid you would throw something at them.)

You regard cancer as an evil that invades and fouls human lives. You want to fight the disease with all the resources of science, of personality, and of faith. But you do not buy the idea that miniature devils are the culprits that cause the problem. A disease requires disciplined scientific research and experimentation, diligent investment of time, brains, energy, and money. Cancer is an adversary of society at large, not only the enemy of its patients.

Prayers and ceremonies protect and enrich life; they are evidence of a greater power than the so-called demons. You celebrate the presence of this power as you confront the reality of cancer; you choose not to waste spiritual or emotional energies and rituals on minor skirmishes with underworld figures. You feel that the best way to do battle with cancer is to regard it as a disease rather than a "haunting." You choose not to dignify it by labeling it as a loathsome personality.

You gain confidence from the experience of Paul the apostle who reported that he asked for his "thorn in the flesh" to be removed; the answer he received was a reminder that the grace of God could sustain him—with or without removing the affliction.

But still, you wonder, "Why?"

† † †

"Life has a way of slapping people down or slapping them into shape."

"The most important lessons we learn bring pain."

You affirm both of these statements, but, with a touch of whimsy, you state, "We could have learned the same lessons at a cheaper price, by an easier route."

For I am convinced that
there is nothing
in death or life,
in the realm of spirits
or superhuman powers,
in the world as it is
or the world as it shall be,
in the forces of the universe,
in heights or depths—
nothing in all creation
that can separate us
from the love of God
in Christ Jesus our Lord.

ROMANS 8:38–39 (N.E.B.)

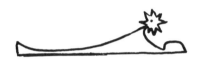

Cancer can KILL me *but it can't get me down*

You are convinced that valuable learnings have taken place. You hold to fewer treasures but you regard them as more precious than before. You discard items of trivia from your collection of values. You choose carefully where you will focus your attention, interests, time, and energy. You have made these discoveries in your first year with cancer, or you have had them reinforced in this year.

But you see these values as salvage, not as the purpose of the illness.

Still you wonder, "Why?"

† † †

By the end of the first year you are still wondering "Why?" But you are beginning to see that the question "Why?"—although unavoidable—is not as productive as the question "So what?" You can make firm statements in answer to that question!

You have cancer, *so what*?

So, you know with gruesome certainty that life is limited, that it is dangerous to take life for granted.

You have cancer, so you want to live as fully as you can for as long as you can.

You have cancer, so you develop emergency plans. You do not want to be dismal; you simply want to be practical.

You have cancer, so you want to contribute to research. You want the doctors to learn from your history; and you want to direct funds toward new discoveries.

You have cancer, so you want to share any benefits you get in this process with other people who go through similar experiences.

You have cancer, so you want to live in such a way that life will not be terror or fear for your children.

You have cancer, so you want to demonstrate the fact that victorious living is possible even in misery and limitation.

You have cancer, so you hope to help overcome public opinion which dictates that all cancer patients are "terminal cases," to be put on the shelf and protected from normal delights and frustrations.

You have cancer, so you rely on spiritual resources and human support, knowing that healing comes through people—professional and nonprofessional.

You have cancer, so you respond to the Biblical view that God enters into and lives in the miseries of human life—redeeming heartache and pain, wringing good out of evil, giving glorious companionship and strength to people who hurt.

You have cancer, so you pray that a miracle of healing will occur, that your concerns and the concerns of other people will be healing forces for all who are ailing, that the "cure" for cancer will be discovered promptly, that life will be rich both now and always.

And still, you wonder, "Why?"

At the End of the First Year

WHERE ARE YOU now that you have reached the end of the first year and L has handed you an azalea and a note: "I had to get you something alive for your celebration"?

You are still doing the things you have been doing all through the year—muddling, leaning, reaching, confronting, wondering.

But you are also putting your discoveries together in new packages. You continue to pack and unpack and re-pack these valuables.

At this point, you are using them and giving them away in these six clusters:

† † †

You meet and absorb and accept experiences that could rub you out.

What happens to you when you are stricken?

You go numb. You hurt. You scream—or you want to scream and cuss. You laugh. You cry. You worry and fret. You struggle and pray. You lecture yourselves. You work. You try to sleep it off. You go into shock. You feel sorry for yourselves. You pretend that you are okay. You fall out. You get up and keep going.

At the end of your first year, you are still rolling with the punches and wondering how to get your balance.

You find strange comfort. Biblical characters who had little or no choice except to "take it" becomes heroes for you. Without claiming parallel suffering, you expand your admiration for Job; he insisted that he did not deserve the mess he lived through. You remember that Moses and Jeremiah and others did not want to take on their "fate"; they resisted the painful service to which they were called. You develop a new appreciation for the combination of "giving in" and determination in the prayer of Jesus, "Not as I will but as thou wilt." (KJV)

You begin to see that accepting and absorbing are valid responses to the inevitable.

Also, by the end of the first year, you realize that you are finite creatures, subject to decay and frustrations. This rediscovery helps you face the possibility of death; it also allows you to accept help, to admit that you are dependent. Despite the fact that your health has improved steadily through the year, you are painfully aware that disaster can strike again—sooner or later, with more or less deadly effect. You are not comfortable with these facts, but you now know that the facts are inescapable. In other words, you accept living-with-turmoil, living-with-uncertainty, living-with-restrictions. But you don't fall in love with turmoil, uncertainty, restrictions; they continue as personal, internalized fences against which you strain. They are unwelcome but inescapable companions.

Now, at the end of the first year of living with cancer, you are blending elements which you once regarded as incompatible—joy and hurt, tears and laughter, today and eternity, worship and play.

When you encounter normal aches and pains, you tremble; they could be danger signals; the cancer may be on the rampage. You depend on the doctor's reassurance to regain your perspectives, to see that you are "doing well." You are glad to hear him say that you can expect ailments unrelated to your major disease. At the same time, you gain confidence that the drugs are working for your benefit and that routine living is an accomplishment. You are forming a new blend—dependence and victory!

At the end of the year, you are operating under a discipline of drugs, scheduled rest, and regular medical checkups. As you step through this imposed regimen, you are quietly and noisily celebrating. You find that you are free to enjoy life, even while you are following instructions. You are forming other new blends—freedom and restrictions, celebration and discipline.

Another cancer patient says soberly, "I've buried many people who pitied me when my malignancy was discovered." His tone blended self-respect with concern for partners in suffering and with thankfulness for his progress. And while you too encounter the ups and downs, while you reach out to colleagues in misery, while you offer thanks for your good fortune, you too are creating new blends of realities—new, at least, for you, in this particular version.

Although you nurture your hatred for cancer and its dangers, by the end of your first year, you are beginning to benefit from your experience of conflict with the foe. You have suffered blows, you have been reeling from them; and you are still here to tell about it and to accept what the future brings.

† † †

You focus attention on people, not on their problems.

At the beginning of your first year, you were overwhelmed at the kindness of people. Several completely dropped what they were doing to see about you and your needs. They rallied around the family during your hospitalization; they developed lovely versions of helpfulness. They focused so much attention on you that they neglected their regular commitments. You temporarily (and gladly) suspended your negative views of human nature, and you were glad to benefit from inspired human generosity.

In response and as a sequel, you devised ways to help when the occasion arose. Of course, you have tried to thank people for their kindness; but you have also been aware that the best expression of gratitude is passing the kindness on to someone else. You have joined this chain of concern whenever people faced even minor skirmishes with cancer. A friend had a "bad looking" mole removed by surgery; there was a three-day wait for the appointment and then a further wait for results from tests. You reached out, though your words were clumsy and your presence frightening. Another neighbor confronted the possibility of "bad news" after routine surgery; she leaned on you for resources when you had none to spare. But you took your position in the network of comradeship and stood there, feeling useless but rightly placed.

In need of special attention, you have been the person in the center. There, you received what you needed through people. Since these dramatic experiences, you reciprocate by quickly placing distressed people at the center of your attention. You do not find or furnish solutions to their problems, but you manage to focus attention on the people.

Even in the more intimate circle of the family, relationships have taken on new values, new excitement. Routine events take on special significance, because you know that they could have been tainted with grief. Annual events, traditionally important, have now become family festivals, rather than quiet nods at the calendar.

Evening prayers, commonplace conversations, moments of decision, times for planning—all these have echoed with the importance of the family's life together. Haunted by the knowledge that this life was almost disrupted, you discover hidden treasures in ordinary places. Both of you enter more wholeheartedly into the "firsts" of your teenagers, and the liveliness of your younger son. When occasions—anniversaries, birthdays, Christmas, Easter—arrive, you are almost giddy about "togetherness." You notice, more readily than before, that these are times when normal values come out for inspection and celebration.

You establish your certainty that the core realities are ties that bind people together. The family is your most intense experience of this reality; but the same reality is also reflected in your ties with others. When called on—to carry the freight of distress—the strength of these ties has been confirmed and exercised.

You lose your balance when you let problems outshine personalities—and the links that connect them.

By the end of your first year of living with cancer, you are identifying the fact that cancer is a villain because it disrupts ties that are holy. On the other hand, you have gone through an experience with this villain, and the experience has endorsed the sacredness of human relations.

You also look with fresh insight at the importance of work Jesus did with his intimate associates. He diligently built ties between himself and his special group of followers. He took time and invested energy in visits with Mary and Martha; he quieted Martha's frenzy about necessary "business."

You hope that you will continue to emphasize the value of people and to keep problems on the fringe of your attention.

† † †

Your sense of purpose provides strength to lift your burdens.

Since you have important things to do, you can ignore some of your problems. And as you gain freedom from your illness, you have places to use your powers.

You are eager to be a party to your teenagers' move into adulthood, so you emphasize their growth rather than your illness. You want to provide a secure atmosphere at home, so you turn your strength in the direction of happy, supportive family events. You encourage them to invite their teenage groups in; you are glad that they are developing valuable adult friendships.

You want to contribute to the church, since it has been a shaping and supporting force in your life, so you concentrate on service from your position as a ruling elder in your congregation. Other people may not realize it, but you are drawing resources for this service from your trauma at the beginning of the year. The dramatic experience itself becomes a base for a ministry to people. You received encouragement, generous help, and steadying love when you were in distress; now you are ready to pass your appreciation on—in the shape of encouragement, help, and love. You do not announce it, but you regard your committee assignments as more than routine duties; they have become channels through which you distribute the strength you are given. You also find ways for your influence to reach beyond your particular congregation; your experience and its benefits are becoming assets for the larger community of faith.

One of your immediate goals is to use your energy to fight your way back to good health. Another is to pick up the normal pieces of life and get them into shape.

One of your discoveries in this year is that power is provided for healing and for mission at the same time. In fact, you doubt that the two can be separated. When you are serving, the service helps the healing process. You experience a boomerang effect; in your weakness you are called to exercise your God-given powers; these powers increase; they dispel your weakness and push the disease into retreat.

One of your dreams is that you will make contributions to the large-scale attack on cancer. Of course, you do this by financial gifts for cancer research. In addition, you like to think that the medical profession is learning from your experience and that their learnings will help other patients. You needed mental, emotional, spiritual resources; you want to help other patients find them too. You interpret your experience, hoping that others who read it can cut short some of the distress you have stumbled through.

Another of your long-range hopes is that the "public mind" can be changed about cancer. Each time someone tells you that you are looking good, you assure them that you are feeling better than you look. You trust that, in these responses, you are whittling away the general attitude which regards the cancer patient as "a hopeless case," to be tolerated and pitied until the end. Each time someone speaks of the statistic, "One person in four can expect to have cancer," you want to remind the world that one cancer patient in three can expect successful treatment. As you prepare this book, you are surprised at the pain in recalling your own past. On the other hand, you are convinced that the recalling-and-writing pains are a worthwhile sacrifice and a proper way of sharing your pilgrimage. You keep at it, because cancer patients and their people need the encouragement. You want the effort to produce new understandings of the disease and new resources for fighting it.

Still another of your desires is to encourage others—patients and nonpatients—to find worthwhile projects, causes, missions, ministries that will overshadow feelings, disappointments, frustrations, pains, limitations.

You want to assure "the world" that these goals, discoveries, dreams, hopes are forces that invigorate the cancer patient to lift burdens, to carry loads.

† † †

The future invades your present scene.

How do you keep life going when a dark shadow lies across it? You move ahead.

The answer sounds simple, even sensible; but you feel both pressure and delight as you give this answer and try to stay honest. After his laryngectomy, a man wrote that he had no choice but to move ahead into speech therapy. You attempt to build up

109

supplies of patience, but you find that there is no way except to take one day at a time; slowly, one step becomes not only enough but a leap into the future.

The struggle with ultimates is one way that the future invades you. Death can no longer be regarded as a remote probability; it becomes a threatening presence. Thinking about the meaning of life cannot be put off; you are in the process of *deciding* the meaning of life by the way you use each slice of time. Vague dread about widowhood, about funeral plans, about the education of your children—all these take shape as concrete plans. You are dealing with the future, not putting it off.

At the same time, you are making another response. You dare to *act* on your convictions about ultimate realities—love, joy, confidence, freedom, service, faith, unity, peace, wholeness. You dare to regard these future realities as current possibilities. Eventually, you say, love will be the dominant force in human life; well, now is the time to put that love into practice. Eventually, you say, peace will prevail; now is the time to build peace. Eventually, freedom will come; but the only time you have to liberate or be liberated is now. Eventually, people will be made whole; but if you are to "have life, and have it abundantly," you can have it now. Your situation dares you to live the future in the present moment.

You do not want to be hypnotized by visions of the future, to make this life insignificant. You know that various religions, Christianity included, have produced colorful pictures of the future. The pictures include golden streets, feasting, angelic choirs, glistening garments, quiet and rest, erotic splendors, gloating success. You recognize that these dreams came to people who were oppressed and deprived; such visions made miseries tolerable. Your concept of the future is not so tied to specific pictures; nevertheless, you do have firm hopes that the future will correct, fulfill, and redeem the present. You base your confidence on the fact that, in Jesus, God defeated the worst enemy, death. For that reason, you are sure that illness will be finally healed and that persons will be fully whole in whatever future life God provides. Meanwhile, you celebrate the certainty that God is working *now*—to bring freedom, joy, harmony, community, and health to all people.

Those involved in the battle with cancer are engaged in twin processes: "buying time" for cancer patients by extending their lives until "the cure" is found; enriching those lives by improving their quality—helping patients with attitudes, services, treatments, drugs, equipment.

Also, you are convinced that miracles are possible. You are even convinced that a miracle is possible in your own life. Even while dreading the dismal possibilities, you dare to act on the possibility of the miraculous, NOW.

† † †

Within limits, you can take initiatives; restrictions do not destroy your freedoms.

She was eighty-one years old when she moved, after living in a small town for more than fifty years. She was recently widowed, she was crippled, and she explained that she was "industrially blind." She could type and she could use the telephone; she lived alone. Within six weeks after her arrival, she had contacted all the blind people in her new home county; she arranged for each of them to have a record player; and she volunteered to order records from the state distributing center that served the sightless. She learned, and she was teaching anyone who wanted to learn, that human beings are creative agents, even when their faculties are limited.

Paul the apostle wrote that he could be content whatever the circumstances. His restless, vigorous spirit found outlets, even when he was under pressure of criticism, when he was confined to prison, when his thorn in the flesh bothered him.

In the Biblical account of creation, God is described as the personality in control, designing-shaping-energizing. He is also portrayed as choosing to make human beings in his own image. This portrait of the Creator shows him giving his own creative power to people; but it also describes limits within which people are to exercise this power. As you move through this first year of living with cancer, you find that you often need these Biblical reminders of necessary restrictions, but you also need the reminders of your freedom to use creativity.

With cancer hovering over you, you wonder how you can exercise your God-given initiatives. You decide to trust the doctors, your feelings, your convictions, yourselves. You design ways in which you can move forcefully into the future. You take on disciplines without wasting energy on resentment. You elect not to be passive personalities in the

111

fight with cancer, and you know that you are fortunate in having the freedom and the strength to choose to fight. When examinations produce no exciting news, you take the reports as endorsements of progress, and you move ahead. You pray for the effectiveness of the drugs and you pray for large doses of determination.

You see that you benefit from the work of creative agents in this first year. You are supported by physicians who are creative in the art of healing. You depend on the creative care of people.

You, also, look for and find opportunities to be creative: with your family, your friends, your work. As long as there is room for this creative force to work, you can stand the limitations

† † †

You are not alone; people and God stay with you.

"They" say that pain is private and that it is intensified by loneliness. In contrast, you have been given steady partnerships through this year.

Your devotion to each other has been strengthened by the stress. The unity in your marriage has withstood the pressures and has developed new flexibility. To begin with, you experienced the initial shock as a blow to each of you, to you as a couple, and to your whole family—not only to you the patient in the hospital. You acted on previous promises not to keep secrets from each other. You decided together how to interpret your situation to other people. You chose the pieces of information which you would keep private. With each other, you have laughed and cried about the indignity of the proctoscopic exam, about unfortunate remarks from people, about your dreams and fears. You have developed skills in "leveling" about your feelings, even when you know that reports of these feelings will hurt your partner. The quality of your marriage—and of other people's marriages—is more significant because of this year's experience. "Partnership" hardly describes your view of marriage; "mutual life" is a little more adequate.

Although you have, all along, emphasized the importance of love and of trustworthy relationships between people, you have been astonished this year at the importance of human ties. Telephone calls have become much more than technological contacts; they have taken on almost sacramental meaning, as people signal their deep involvement in your life. Gifts, flowers, conversations, food, letters—these gestures have carried the cargo and have lifted some of your burdens. Through the years and through this crisis year, you have been surrounded by people. They have helped you develop your inner strength, have counted on you to help them develop theirs; and they have confirmed this union by their presence through the crisis. Your children's reaction to trauma, for instance, has been reassuring. They have shown that they are able to contend with the pressures of life, that they want you around, and that they are a source of real strength.

You have discovered that ties of friendship and love enable you to benefit from the presence of people, even when they are across the country from you—or across the ocean. You sense their companionship when they are not in the same room or the same town or the same condition with you.

You hate to admit—or claim—it, but you are more pious than you were before. By "pious" you mean "sensitive to the presence of God." You do not see piety as a set of rules to follow or series of spiritual tricks to perform. Instead you regard piety as gratitude to God soaking into ordinary activities and taking shape as prayer and hard work. You suspect that you appear to be more devout, but you do not ask anyone to verify this: neither do you want to march around under a banner marked "devout" or "pious" or "holy." On the other hand, you do want your companionship with God to be evident; you hope that others will detect his presence when you are around. He holds you up; his presence is your cure for loneliness and your assurance of life. You are learning to lean gracefully.

You can afford to lean, not because you are sensitive to the presence of God, but because he has let you know he is available. The chief location of his availability is the personality and career of Jesus. He demonstrated God's permanent concern in that specific lifetime. His life was spent among plain people; he used his energies for their benefit—teaching, preaching, healing. He identified with the needy and the irreligious. He carried this identification all the way into his death. The Apostles' Creed uses the statement, "He descended into hell." You understand this statement to mean that he moved all the way through the miseries of human existence. Therefore, you can rely on his companionship in the future—pleasant or unpleasant. You can trust him not to pull back when the going is rough or when the delights are sweeping you off your feet. He has been through this territory before, and he is qualified to give you the companionship you need.

† † †

You start into the second year of living with cancer.

Expecting and enjoying rich life, you are living under the threat of death.

Begging for a complete and permanent cure, you are living in comfortable health.

Gobbling up each moment's satisfaction, you are living with intense hungers.

Embracing uncertainty, you are living with lofty hopes.

Sampling both dread and joy, you are living for worthy tasks.

Remembering misery, you are living in gratitude.

Arguing with unalterable facts, you are living as students needing to learn.

Depending on external support, you are living by feeble determination.

Shaking from its tremors, you are living on top of cancer.

Hallelujah!

Epilogue

WHILE THIS BOOK was in preparation, both Grandmother Shaw and Grandmother Turnage died of cancer. Of course, the project was delayed.

By the time the book was finished, Anne, you reached the second anniversary of your surgery. Extensive tests, including a biopsy, a liver scan, and new blood tests, produced reports that you are clear of tumors. You continue on the same program of medication and medical care and in the same realistic jubilation.

Again, Hallelujah!